'Well, things are very different now. I know what I want out of life,' Samantha said.

Luke surveyed her with cool detachment. 'And just what *do* you want, Samantha?'

'A lot of things you wouldn't even begin to appreciate,' she retorted sharply. 'However, first and foremost I want a divorce!'

'Are you planning to marry someone else?'

She cursed inwardly as she felt her cheeks redden. No, she wasn't—not at the moment, anyway—although she had no intention of telling him so. Besides, he had a nerve questioning her about her future matrimonial plans—especially since he was the one who was travelling around the Caribbean with a flashy blonde girlfriend in tow!

'Well?'

'If...well, if I am thinking of getting married again, it has absolutely nothing to do with you,' she said firmly.

'Oh, no?' Luke gave a harsh bark of sardonic laughter as he spun on his heels and strode over towards the door. 'If you want my consent to a divorce, I think you'll find that—as your present husband—it has *everything* to do with me!'

HURRICANE!

BY

MARY LYONS

MILLS & BOON LIMITED
ETON HOUSE   18-24 PARADISE ROAD
RICHMOND   SURREY   TW9 1SR

*First published in Great Britain 1988
by Mills & Boon Limited*

© Mary Lyons 1988

*Australian copyright 1988
Philippine copyright 1988
This edition 1988*

ISBN 0 263 76135 5

*Set in Times Roman 10 on 11½ pt
01-8811-58697 C*

Made and printed in Great Britain

CHAPTER ONE

'HURRICANE?' Samantha frowned, interrupting her pre-flight check of the Cessna's fuselage. 'Are you sure, Leroy? I haven't heard any reports that Hurricane Hannah is likely to be coming our way.'

The mechanic shrugged his shoulders, swiftly un-coupling the flexible gasoline pipe from the aircraft, and winding it back on to the tanker containing the high octane fuel.

'I don't reckon there's any need for you to worry, Miss Ward.' A reassuring grin spread over his dark face as he glimpsed the apprehension lurking in the depths of her wide green eyes. 'I ain't heard nothing official. It's only my old granny up to her prophesying again—that's all!'

'You rotter! You really had me worried for a moment,' Samantha laughed, giving the rudder a waggle as she resumed her inspection of the small twin-engined aero-plane. 'Your grandmother seems to enjoy spreading doom and gloom. According to her, life here on Antigua is nothing more or less than a modern version of Sodom and Gomorrah! Didn't she forecast that the world was definitely coming to an end, some time last July?'

'Yeah, but as she says—everyone's entitled to one little mistake!' Leroy chuckled, jumping up into the cab of the tanker and giving a friendly wave as he drove away across the tarmac.

Bending down to check the undercarriage, Samantha was still smiling as she rose and put on her sunglasses to look up at the wide expanse of clear blue sky over Vere Bird Airport. It was a perfect day for flying. There

5

wasn't a cloud in sight, and only a slight breeze to disturb
the fiery cloud of burnished, copper-coloured hair which
tumbled down about her shoulders. Glancing idly over
at a white, unmarked Hawker Siddeley executive jet as
it touched down and taxied across the tarmac, her gaze
swept on towards the large, American Airlines Boeing
which had landed some time ago.

'Come on...come on!' she muttered, watching impatiently as the last of the passengers descended from
the plane and made their way over to the airport
buildings. It was frustrating to know that there was
nothing she could do to speed up the arrival of the two
people she was expecting. Even if they weren't likely to
be subjected to Customs inspection, her in-transit passengers still had to wait alongside everyone else to claim
their baggage in the Arrivals Hall.

It was beginning to look as if she'd made a mistake
in listening to the desperate plea of Mike Donald, the
local manager of Caribbean Air Transport—known
around the islands as CAT—when she had flown into
Antigua this morning. With two of his aeroplanes temporarily out of commission, one undergoing routine
maintenance, and the other waiting for some vital spare
parts from America, Mike had been a worried man.

'You know how it is, Samantha. It's the beginning of
the high season out here, and if we default on this con-
tract with the big travel companies, they won't hesitate
to give their business to some of the larger outfits, like
Carib Aviation or LIAT. So, how about being a real good
pal, and taking a couple of tourists in your plane when
you fly back to St Pauls this afternoon?'

Since it was Mike who had first taught her to fly, she
hadn't felt able to refuse such a reasonable request, and
there was no doubt that the fee for transporting his passengers would come in very useful. However, being a 'real

good pal' was one thing—waiting around for over an hour with no shelter from the blazing sun was quite another! It was maddening to be stuck here on the concrete runway, especially as she could have been back on the island by now, and trying to bring some sort of order into the chaotic affairs of the Hamilton Plantation Hotel. Despite working in the hotel office until very late last night, Samantha still hadn't managed to make any headway in sorting out the confusion. It was beginning to look as if Aunt Emily hadn't attempted even the simplest bookkeeping, let alone kept a proper set of accounts, for the last ten years. However, fretting about the amount of work to be done wasn't going to get her anywhere. She would just have to hope that nothing had gone drastically wrong since she'd left this morning.

Samantha sighed. Trying to run the hotel while Aunt Emily was in hospital, and the need to constantly reassure her aunt that it wasn't going to rack and ruin in the absence of that formidable woman, seemed to be taking up every spare moment of her time; time that she ought to be giving to her own business. Although she had full confidence in the girls running her gift shops on the nearby islands, they couldn't be expected to manage everything. It had meant a great deal of hard, exhausting work over the last four years to achieve her present satisfactory turnover, but it was a heavily competitive business and one she couldn't afford to neglect for too long.

It wasn't that she minded the extra amount of work and effort involved in running the small hotel. It was nothing when set beside the strong bond of love and gratitude she felt for the autocratic, elderly woman who had provided the only real, stable home life that Samantha had ever known. If only Aunt Emily could be persuaded to take the opportunity of her enforced stay in hospital to have a good rest, and concentrate on getting well. However, the chances of that happening were just about zero! Samantha thought wryly, recalling the visit to her aunt earlier this morning.

'You've got to get me out of this damn place—or I'll go stark staring mad!' Aunt Emily had demanded, angrily brushing a forceful hand through her short, wiry hair, which had once been the same fiery colour as Samantha's, but which was now a pure white halo framing her strong, hawk-like features.

'Oh, come on, Aunt Em—you know I can't do that.' Samantha gazed sympathetically down at the slight figure in the large hospital bed. 'You've had a very nasty fall, and a broken hip is no joke—especially not at your age.'

'Nonsense! I'm not a day over sixty-five...'

'Seventy-two!'

'...and I'm as fit as a fiddle,' her aunt continued, blithely ignoring her niece's dry interjection. 'God knows, I've already broken most of the bones in my body one way or another, so what does a hip-joint matter?'

'It's no good glaring at me like a ferocious tiger,' Samantha retorted. 'I don't blame you for feeling fed up, but it's a super hospital and you're getting the very best care and attention.'

'But the hotel...'

'There's nothing you can do about the hotel at the moment,' Samantha said firmly. 'Here you are, and here I'm afraid you'll have to stay, until you're back on your feet and the doctors say you can return to the island.'

'*Doctors!*' The older woman snorted. 'Everyone in this place seems far too young. Even my surgeon looks as if he's only just started to shave—practically fresh out of the egg and still got the yolk on him, if you ask me. So, what's he likely to know about anything?'

Samantha sighed and prayed for patience. She loved her aunt very much, but it didn't blind her to the fact that Emily Ward was a fiercely autocratic and difficult old woman at the best of times. Unfortunately, now that she was virtually confined to her hospital bed, she was fast becoming a holy terror.

'Your doctor knows enough to be one of the most highly qualified surgeons in the Caribbean, and *you* know that you shouldn't be smoking one of those filthy cigars,' Samantha said briskly, reaching over to remove the cheroot from between her aunt's thin, bony fingers.

'That's all I need...an ungrateful niece taking away the only real pleasure I've got left in life.' Emily Ward gave a heavy sigh, closing her eyes as she lay back against the pillows. 'And a visit yesterday from that pansy boy-friend of yours didn't make me feel any better, I can tell you,' she grumbled.

'Who...? Gerald...?' Samantha looked at her with exasperation. 'It was very kind of him to call and see you, and he's certainly not a "pansy"!'

'Hmm. You could have fooled me. I knew his grand-father, and he was just the same—a rich, idle layabout.'

'You're being very unfair,' Samantha said curtly. Gerald Robarts might be rich, but he was far from idle, as her aunt knew very well. Sailing that huge yacht of his around the world for the past two years hadn't exactly been a soft occupation. And just because he had decided to berth his boat in English Harbour for the past few months, well...it certainly didn't mean that he de-served to be called a layabout. The plain fact was that her aunt had taken an instant dislike to Gerald, and their subsequent meetings had done nothing to dispel her animosity.

The older woman fixed her niece with a beady eye. 'Getting serious about him, are you?'

'Not really, I . . .'

'He wants to marry you, doesn't he?'

'Well . . .'

'Does he know that you're still married to another man?'

Samantha's cheeks flushed. 'Well, I haven't exactly . . .'

'Hah! I thought so. Has it occurred to you that Luke might well have something to say about this romance of yours?'

'It has absolutely nothing to do with Luke!' Samantha snapped angrily. 'And I'm not having a "romance" with Gerald. We're just good friends, that's all.'

'Oh, yes? I wonder where I've heard *that* old cliché before?' the old woman muttered sarcastically.

Samantha sighed, and prayed for patience. 'Come on, Aunt Em. You know as well as I do that, after four years on my own, the question of my so-called marital status is nothing but a mere technicality. If I haven't got around to getting a divorce, it's . . . well, it's just because I've been too busy, that's all.' She moved over to fill her aunt's glass with some orange juice. 'I know you don't like him, but Gerald's really far too nice to have upset you like this. So, what's the real problem? Did you have a bad night?'

'Not too good,' the older woman admitted reluctantly. 'All the doctors can do is to mutter some tommy-rot about elderly bones taking longer to knit. It's been two weeks and they still can't—or won't—say when I can go home. How on earth am I supposed to run the hotel from here?' she added irritably.

'The simple answer is that you're not. The hotel is running like clockwork, so all you have to do is to relax and give your hip a chance to mend.'

'Clockwork . . .? Hah! I may be old, but I'm not senile!' Emily Ward gave a harsh bark of laughter. 'And if you hadn't been so darn proud—not to say downright stubborn—and had let me ask Luke for enough money to do up the hotel, I might not be lying here and worrying myself sick.'

'Oh, no...' Samantha groaned. 'You're not going on about that *again*, are you?'

'Certainly I am,' her aunt retorted. 'Not only is Luke Brandon as rich as Croesus, but he and I always got along well together. You might not want to have anything to do with your ex-husband, but I don't have any scruples about getting my hands on some of his money! God knows—as far as he's concerned, it wouldn't mean more than a few cents from the petty cash.'

Samantha's lips tightened. 'I've had my say on that subject, and there's no way I'm ever going to change my mind. Now, for heaven's sake stop worrying about the hotel. I've got everything under control.'

'Humph...!'

Samantha had ignored her aunt's grunt of derision, determined to maintain the fiction that all was well. What else could she do? she asked herself for the umpteenth time, leaning against the Cessna's wing and staring blindly across the tarmac at a large jet preparing for take-off. She didn't suppose that she had fooled Aunt Emily—not for one minute!—but there was nothing to be achieved by relating the fact that the ancient generator had broken down again. Or that Thomas, the temperamental chef, had taken a bottle of rum to bed with him last night, and had been still out for the count when she had left this morning. In fact, considering the general run-down condition of the hotel, it was a mercy that nothing more drastic had happened since her aunt's accident.

Not for the first time during these past few weeks, she found herself fervently wishing that Aunt Emily had sold

Hamilton Plantation Hotel years ago. Named after
Alexander Hamilton, who was supposed to have lived
there when a young boy on the island of St Pauls—a
fact that Samantha privately thought didn't bear too
much scrutiny!—the hotel was set beside a long white
sandy beach. The old grey-stoned plantation house,
which formed the main part of the hotel, was surrounded by palm trees which also sheltered and gave
shade to the twenty small guest bungalows scattered
around the grounds between the main house and the sea.
It was an idyllic situation, and she had always supported
her aunt's resolute refusal to consider selling what was,
to all intents and purposes, their home. However, it was
swiftly becoming clear to Samantha that not only was
the hotel running at a loss—and had been doing so for
the past three or four years—but that Aunt Emily was
now becoming too old and infirm to cope with the
mounting problems.

Her aunt had been right about the crying need for
extra finance—there was no doubt that the place needed
to have a fortune spent on it. However, since there was
no hope of either of them being able to lay their hands
on the amount of money required, there wasn't much
point in thinking about it. As for the suggestion that she
should go cap in hand to her ex-husband...? She'd rather
die than face that sort of humiliation! When she had
walked out on Luke Brandon, she had also left behind
in his grimly austere New York apartment all her clothes,
furs and jewellery—even her wedding ring. She hadn't
needed or wanted his money and possessions four years
ago, and she *certainly* didn't need or want them now!
Besides...

The sound of an approaching vehicle brought her
abruptly back to the present, and she looked up as a
small van screeched to a halt beside the Cessna. A slim,

dark girl, wearing the blue and white CAT uniform, threw open the passenger door and jumped down on to the tarmac.

'Hi, Sam. Sorry we're late,' she called out, turning to help an elderly couple out of the van and into the aeroplane, before directing the driver to stow their luggage in the aircraft hold.

Samantha grinned at Natalie, Mike Donald's assistant, as the girl ducked under the wing and handed her a clipboard. 'You can tell Mike that I'm planning to give him a hefty kick in the shins! After standing out here for over an hour, I was just about to send out a search party.'

'It wouldn't have done you much good if you had.' Natalie gave her a wry smile. 'Mrs Thomson is a very sweet old lady, but after I'd spent almost half an hour trying to find a suitcase she insisted was missing, she suddenly remembered that she hadn't brought it with her, after all!'

'One of those days, huh?'

'You're so right,' the other girl groaned with feeling. 'Thank goodness you agreed to help us out.'

'Hang on a minute.' Samantha frowned down at the passenger list on the clipboard. 'I thought I was only supposed to be carrying two passengers—Mr and Mrs Thomson. So, how come the number has suddenly grown to four?'

'Oh, yes. We're sorry about that, but we only got the telex this morning, and...'

'...and your boss can't stand the thought of empty seats on an aeroplane!' Samantha added with grim amusement. 'Well, if Mike expects me to stand out here, twiddling my thumbs and waiting for this "Miss van de Burgh and companion" to turn up, he's definitely got another think coming!'

'Relax—they'll be here in a minute,' Natalie said, pointing towards the Hawker Siddeley executive jet, which had landed earlier.

Samantha turned to gaze at the distant figures of a man and a woman, standing beside the sleek white aeroplane while their luggage was unloaded. Idly following their progress as they began to walk across the concrete runway towards the Cessna, she slowly stiffened, her gaze narrowing as she peered through the shimmering haze of the fierce sunlight.

Surely that couldn't be...? No, of course not! It simply wasn't possible...

The colour draining from her face, her stomach gave a sudden lurch of fear and apprehension, her pulse racing out of control as the two people drew nearer. Rigid with shock, it was some moments before her stunned mind was able to comprehend the evidence of her own eyes. And then she knew, with an absolute and sickening certainty, that there was no possibility of a mistake. There, turning his tanned, arrogant face to smile briefly at his blonde companion, was Luke Brandon—the very last man in the world she had ever expected, or wanted, to see.

'*Oh, my God...!*' she whispered, helplessly clutching the clipboard to her breast, as if to ward off the evil eye.

'Mmm...my sentiments exactly!' Natalie giggled, standing on tiptoe to peer over the wing, her eyes devouring the lithe, masculine grace of the tall dynamic figure approaching the aeroplane. 'Oh, boy—now that's what I call a *real* man!'

Paralysed by shock, it was a few seconds before Samantha was able to pull herself together. 'Quick, you've got to help me!' she hissed, grabbing hold of the other girl's arm and dragging her back against the plane's fuselage, well out of sight of Luke and his companion.

'Hey! What's suddenly come over you?' Natalie grumbled. 'I was only saying...'

'You can say anything you like, just as long as you make sure that man doesn't get into the aeroplane for five minutes, OK?' Samantha demanded urgently, only too well aware that it was a matter of seconds before she was likely to be confronted by her ex-husband.

Natalie stared at her in puzzlement. 'I thought you wanted to take off as soon as possible. So why...?'

'Never mind the ''whys and wherefores'',' Samantha snapped. 'I'm only asking you to keep that damned man on the tarmac for a few minutes, that's all. Why don't you drop a suitcase on his foot, or chat him up, or...or do the dance of the seven veils, if necessary,' she added wildly. 'Just as long as you manage to distract his attention.'

'OK, OK—calm down!' Natalie grinned, running her hands down over her hips to straighten her skirt. 'I don't know what's going on, but if you want me to ''chat up'' that gorgeous man—no sweat, honey. It'll be a real pleasure!'

Her heart pounding like a sledge-hammer, Samantha waited until the girl had gone around to the other side of the aircraft, before leaping up on to the wing and jerking open the door by the pilot's seat.

Feverishly searching the confined space—Oh, help! Where on earth was it?—she finally located the old baseball cap she occasionally wore when flying. Ignoring the startled glances of Mr and Mrs Thomson, she threw herself down into her seat, quickly scooping up her long red hair and jamming the cap down on her head.

Whether her rough and ready attempt to disguise herself was going to work would be very much in the lap of the gods. But there had to be a good chance that Luke wouldn't recognise her, she thought, turning up her collar to hide her neck and pushing her dark glasses firmly down on her nose, especially if she made sure that all he saw of the pilot was her back view. Besides, he would hardly be expecting to meet the wife he hadn't seen for four years on the tarmac of an airport in the Caribbean—and certainly not at the controls of an aeroplane! It was only after she had run away from Luke, and with the entrancing prospect of having the use of her aunt's private plane, that she had decided to have the lessons which had led to her gaining her pilot's licence two years ago.

She had to swallow quickly, fighting against a bubble of hysterical laughter at the thought of her ex-husband's reaction to her baggy white overalls, and the fact that her feet were encased in an old pair of sneakers. The immaculately clothed Luke Brandon, who regularly appeared in the list of the top ten best-dressed men in America, would have had an apoplectic fit if she'd ever waltzed down Fifth Avenue attired like this!

Oh, lord! She had to pull herself together—and fast! Her teeth seemed to be clattering like castanets, her hands shaking as if she had St Vitus's dance as she swiftly closed the door beside her and adjusted her harness. If she didn't watch out, she was going to have this plane yawing all over the sky, and that would endanger not only the lives of her passengers, but also any other aircraft in her vicinity.

Desperately trying to banish from her mind the traumatic effect of Luke's sudden appearance, Samantha forced herself to concentrate on the routine pre-flight checks. It was only when she was in contact with the control tower, and she felt the aircraft move slightly as Luke and his companion came aboard, that her voice faltered slightly. However, there was so much to do during the next ten minutes that it wasn't until they were airborne and flying high over the blue Caribbean Sea that she was able to begin thinking about her predicament.

She hadn't checked the hotel register this morning, but she couldn't recall seeing anything about—what was the woman's name?—Miss van de something-or-other…? And she *certainly* would have noticed a booking for Luke! Samantha settled back in her seat, feeling some of the tension draining out of her body. Her ex-husband—well, they might be technically still married, but he was definitely *'ex'* as far as she was concerned—was undoubtedly booked into one of the hotels on the other side of the island. So, providing she managed to avoid any contact with him when they landed, and kept a very low profile for the next two weeks, there was a good chance of avoiding him altogether.

The rhythmic drone of the plane's engines was helping to calm down her confused emotions, the noise also preventing her from hearing anything more than a faint mumble as the passengers chatted together. For the first time since she'd set eyes on them, she found herself wondering about the woman with Luke. She had been too shocked at his sudden appearance to take much notice of his companion, but from the little she could remember, it looked as if Miss What's-her-name fitted the usual pattern of Luke's girlfriends—tall, blonde and very, very cool. Although, now she came to think about it, Luke had certainly changed his habits. From all she had known of him, both before and during their brief marriage, he had never willingly taken a vacation. It had always been business—first, last and in between. Even on their honeymoon in Europe, when she had suggested that they might break their tour of the capital cities and stay at a quiet beach resort, he had given her a brief,

incredulous smile before going off to yet another of his
interminable business meetings.

It wasn't all Luke's fault, of course. If she hadn't been
so distraught over her father's unexpected death, and so
young and pathetically naïve, she'd have known that she
wasn't able to cope with the Luke Brandons of this
world. In the event, their marriage had proved to be a
disaster. She had been eighteen when she'd married him,
and when she walked out a year later, she'd felt more
like a hundred and two.

The distant sight of a green, palm-fringed island
brought her unhappy thoughts back to the present. There
was no aircraft control on St Pauls and, after circling
the short runway, she brought the Cessna down in a
landing that was, embarrassingly, somewhat bumpier
than usual. Well, considering Luke's completely unexpected arrival, it wasn't surprising, Samantha consoled
herself as a member of the airport staff ran forward to
open the rear door of the aircraft. Keeping her face well
averted, and waiting until the passengers had disem-
barked, she taxied the plane over to the small hangar at
the edge of the field.

During the flight, she had wondered just how she was
going to manage to leave the airport without being seen
by Luke, but in the event it proved to be no problem.
After locking up the plane and securely fastening the
doors of the hangar, she took advantage of the shelter
provided by a scrub hedge forming part of the airport
boundary. Carefully skirting the large hut which served
as the main terminal building, Samantha stuck her head
into the window of a small office, and after a quick word
with one of the Customs and Excise staff, she jumped
into her mini-moke and was soon speeding off down the
road to the hotel. Home and dry! she told herself ten
minutes later, laughing at her fears as she strode through

the hall to reception, where she was promptly and swiftly brought back down to earth with a bump.

'Oh, yes, Mizz Ward. We surely do have some new guests arriving today.' Susie, a local girl who worked in the hotel part-time, gave her a dazzling smile. 'I took the call yesterday afternoon, and I just knew you'd be pleased, 'coz we's now full up.'

'But why on earth didn't you write their names down on the booking form yesterday?' Samantha hissed through clenched teeth.

'Oh, Mizz Ward, you knows my spelling ain't too good. So, I just waits till this morning and asked Lester, the barman, to do it for me.'

As she struggled to control an almost irresistible urge to slap that beaming smile off the stupid girl's face, Samantha realised with a sinking heart that she was well and truly in a mess.

Staring, almost mesmerised, at the entry on the register, the names 'Miss van de Burgh and companion' seemed to be etched in fiery capitals as they leapt off the page towards her. And it didn't take a very high IQ to know exactly who ' . . . and companion' was going to turn out to be! she told herself with grim foreboding.

An hour later, Samantha stood beneath the shower, almost groaning with pleasure as the cool sting of the water revived her tired body. What a day it had been—and it wasn't finished yet, she reminded herself harshly, cursing under her breath at the realisation that she had very little time or space for manoeuvre. Of course, she'd done what she could to alter the staffing arrangements for the evening. Luckily, Penny Bird, her aunt's young manager, had agreed to show Luke and his girlfriend to their respective bungalows, and, after bawling out the chef for last night's drunken orgy, Samantha had finally managed to escape to sanctuary in the old sugar mill.

Turning off the shower and wrapping her slim form in a fluffy towel, Samantha unhooked the hairdryer fixed to the wall of the bathroom and began to blow-dry her long red hair. At least she was safe here—for the moment, anyway.

Restored with loving care by Aunt Emily, the old building had been presented to Samantha when she had returned to the island four years ago. Built by an eighteenth-century plantation owner, it had originally possessed huge wind-vanes which had turned the wooden cogs and iron rollers, whose function was to crush the sugar cane once grown on Hamilton Plantation Estate. Now, its machinery long gone, there was just the one big, circular sitting-room open to the rafters high above, the soaring height and space of the building scarcely impeded by the galleried bedroom which was all that remained of the original second floor, and whose access was via an open mahogany staircase fixed to the side of the circular wall. The bathroom, and the small kitchen, which led off the main sitting-room, were modern and essential additions to the old building. They might have been incongruous in such a setting had not Aunt Emily carefully sited the doors beneath the gallery on the far wall to the main entrance, where they remained largely unnoticed and unseen by the casual visitor.

The sugar mill itself, while only a few yards away from the main plantation house, was completely hidden from sight by a grove of breadfruit trees, underplanted with frangipani and bougainvillaea. It was the only permanent home of her own that Samantha had ever possessed and, when she had returned to the island following the disintegration of her marriage to Luke, much of her misery and unhappiness had been assuaged by the blessed peace and serenity of its ancient stone walls.

However, it was no good thinking she could stay hidden here for very long. With Luke and his girlfriend apparently booked into the hotel for the next two weeks, she really had to come to some sort of decision.

To anyone who didn't know Luke, it would seem quite ridiculous of her to be in such a state of nerves, just because of her ex-husband's sudden arrival on the island. However, those who worked in or had anything to do with Wall Street could tell a different story. The Brandon Effect was what the newspapers called it: the way companies and even well-established institutions would allow themselves to be taken over, caving in without a fight the moment that Luke, in the guise of Brandon-Phillips International, appeared on the financial horizon. Following his uncle, James Phillips', unexpected and early death from a heart attack, and the subsequent epic power struggle for control of the financial conglomerate which comprised Phillips International, Luke had swiftly and ruthlessly expanded his empire; his progress to fame and ever-increasing fortune littered with the debris of those who didn't understand his compulsive urge to win—at whatever cost. Too young to know any better, Samantha now saw that she must have been one of the few people who had ever tried to stand up to him, but even she had been defeated by his refusal to compromise, or to admit that there might possibly be another point of view to that of his own.

It hadn't been like that at the start of their relationship, of course. Luke had seemed so wonderful, so... 'Forget it!' she told herself roughly. There was nothing to be gained by trying to recall her brief, fleeting moments of total happiness. When she had walked out on her marriage, she had locked the door on her memories and deliberately thrown away the key. There was absolutely no point in trying to resurrect something that was dead and buried. She'd be much better employed in trying to decide how to cope with the situation in which she now found herself.

She could, of course, pretend that Luke was a complete stranger, and treat both him and his girlfriend as she did the rest of the guests, in a cool and friendly manner. That would be the sophisticated, worldly approach, but even after four years she wasn't at all sure that she possessed that amount of sophistication!

On the other hand, Luke had never made any effort to follow or get in touch with her after she'd run away—and with his contacts, it wouldn't have been too hard for him to find out exactly where she'd gone to ground. Not that she had expected him to. She had hoped, indeed she had relied on the fact that there was no way he would ever have forgiven such a blow to his self-esteem. So, maybe there was a chance that he would leave the island as soon as he discovered her role in the hotel. And if not . . .?

Switching off the dryer, and brushing out her long hair, Samantha knew that she simply didn't have whatever it took to face two long weeks of Luke's formidable presence. 'You're nothing but a yellow-bellied coward!' she told her white-faced reflection in the mirror, and, despite the obvious truth in the statement, it didn't alter the fact of her overwhelming need to put as much distance as possible between herself and her ex-husband. There was only one obvious solution to her problem, and that was to get away from the island as soon as she could. It was too late to try and arrange anything tonight, especially since she was going to have to be on duty overseeing the dining-room and kitchen. But if she could persuade Penny Bird to hold the fort for a few days, she might be able to come up with some sort of answer.

Preoccupied with trying to solve the problem of exactly where to go to escape Luke, she slipped on a thin, white silk robe and walked slowly through into the sitting-room.

A moment later she stiffened like a wary cat, rigid with a sense of impending danger. A thin thread of tobacco smoke drifted across the dark room, but before the familiar scent reached her—even before her hand moved towards the light switch—she instinctively knew the identity of the tall figure standing in the shadows by the window.

CHAPTER TWO

THE background whirr of the ceiling fan was the only sound to disturb the long, heavy silence as Samantha stared across the room at her husband. Her green eyes were glazed with shock and consternation, and it was some moments before she was able to try and pull her scattered wits together.

'How...how did you get in here?' she demanded huskily.

'That's not a very intelligent question, Samantha,' Luke drawled, stubbing out his thin cigar on a nearby ashtray. 'I came in through the door, of course. I did knock,' he added smoothly, as she opened her mouth to protest. 'But if, as it seems, you were under the shower, you obviously wouldn't have heard me. Don't you think that it might be more sensible, in this dangerous age, if you were to fit a lock to your front door, hmm?'

'Don't worry! If it will keep you out of my home, I'll make sure that I see to it—first thing in the morning!'

'A very sensible decision,' he agreed, giving her a cool smile—a bland assumption of overwhelming superiority which she had always found extremely irritating.

Oh, God—here we go again! Samantha gritted her teeth as she watched the tall, elegant figure who was now walking around the room, regarding his surroundings with considerable interest. Despite their long separation, it seemed that she and Luke had only to be in each other's company for five seconds, and then: wham...! They were right back to square one, resurrecting their old roles of authoritarian teacher versus rebellious pupil. But she'd

24

finally broken out of the mould, she quickly reminded herself. She didn't have to put up with his lectures any more, nor his maddening air of condescension.

'This old sugar mill is really very charming,' he murmured, picking up a cushion to examine its cover more closely. 'Is this an example of the local batik?'

'Yes.'

'It's very attractive,' he added before tossing it back to join the others on the couch.

'Yes, it is,' she snapped impatiently. 'However, I don't for one moment imagine that you've come all this way just to discuss the arts and crafts to be found on this island.'

He gave her a dry, amused glance from beneath his heavy eyelids. 'You're quite right, I haven't.'

'So, why are you here?'

Luke shrugged his broad shoulders. 'For various reasons—mainly to do with business,' he said casually, his tone bland and dismissive as he continued to explore the large room.

She should have remembered that the damn man never gave anything away, Samantha told herself grimly. However, there were one or two pressing questions to which she needed an urgent answer.

'I'm not interested in your business affairs,' she said curtly. 'However, I do want to know...I mean, how did you...?'

'How did I recognise you?' He gave a short bark of sardonic laughter. 'My dear girl! Despite your valiant attempts to disguise yourself in that dreadful old baseball hat, surely you can't have seriously imagined that I wouldn't be able to identify my own wife?'

Since that was exactly what she'd hoped, Samantha stood rooted to the floor, glaring at him with stormy eyes as she mentally struggled to reassess the situation.

It was absolutely sickening to find that all her frantic precautions, all her determined efforts to avoid him, had been a complete and utter waste of time. She had always suspected that he had an almost supernatural ability to see around corners and through walls. And she knew that she wasn't the only one to think so: most of his business competitors had seemed to feel exactly the same way.

He hadn't changed at all, she thought gloomily. Physically, he was perhaps thinner than she remembered; there were a few more few silver strands among the dark hair at his temples, and the lines about his firm, determined mouth seemed to be more deeply etched. But, in essence, he appeared to be very much the same hard, ruthless man from whom she had run away over four years ago.

'What an enterprising girl you've turned out to be!' He gave her a cold, mocking grin. 'I must say that it was a novel experience to take a supposedly routine, scheduled flight—only to find that it was my wife at the controls of the aircraft! You do have a licence to fly that aeroplane, I hope?' he enquired blandly.

'That's not a very intelligent question, Luke,' she retorted, mimicking both the words and tone of voice which he had used earlier.

He suddenly stopped his restless perambulations about the room, turning to stare at her from beneath his heavy eyelids with a deep intensity that she found distinctly unnerving. It was if he was doing some complicated, mental arithmetic, which obstinately refused to add up correctly, and she quickly looked away from those all-seeing, penetrating eyes.

'All right, let's get down to brass tacks,' she said, painfully aware of the breathless, nervous wobble in her voice. 'Why are you here, and what do you want?'

'Maybe I felt, under the circumstances, that it might be easier if we first met in private, rather than among a crowd of guests. As to what I want . . .' He paused, his eyes moving slowly over her slim figure clothed only in the thin silk gown. 'Why should you assume that I want anything?'

Samantha's cheeks burned. If, during the past few years, she had ever wondered about the possibility of meeting Luke again, she had never in her wildest dreams envisaged the present situation, in which she was so clearly at a disadvantage. Suddenly becoming embarrassingly conscious, not only of being naked beneath her robe, but also of her bare feet and the tangled cloud of newly washed hair, it was all she could do to hang on to her temper in the face of Luke's insulting, analytical appraisal.

'OK—so you've called to say "hello",' she said through clenched teeth. 'However, as far as I'm concerned, the next word that comes to mind is— "goodbye".'

'Such a friendly welcome!' he murmured sardonically.

'I don't feel friendly, and you're definitely not welcome,' she retorted quickly, her trembling figure striving to control an increasing tide of fury and resentment at the unfairness of life in general, and Luke in particular.

The room was large, and yet it seemed filled with his presence. His lean, tautly muscled frame clothed in cream linen trousers with a matching short-sleeved, casual shirt, radiated an impression of power and confidence, and there was clearly very little that escaped those piercing blue eyes beneath heavy lids, through which he appeared to survey life with a faintly contemptuous, cynical amusement. Not that she was likely to be fooled by such a false expression, nor by his oh-so-deceptive aura of relaxed, sensual charm, which was already having a most peculiar effect on her pulse-rate, despite the ten feet or so which lay between them. Calm down...keep cool...she warned herself urgently, knowing that she mustn't, not even for one second, forget that Luke Brandon was an extremely dangerous man.

'You've already made your feelings abundantly clear,' he drawled. 'In fact, there is no doubt in my mind that it is you, Samantha, whom I have to thank for the unnecessarily thorough search of both our luggage—and our persons—by the local Customs. Hmm?'

Oh, lord—she'd completely forgotten all about that! Her cheeks reddened beneath Luke's hard scrutiny.

'Perhaps you can enlighten me as to exactly what you told the Customs officers? What were we supposed to be smuggling? Gold, was it—or maybe, diamonds? Well...?' he demanded as she remained silent.

'I—er—I might have said something about drugs...' she muttered, avoiding his gaze and fervently wishing that she'd never given in to such a crazy, mischievous impulse back at the airport.

His lips tightened, his eyes narrowing to chips of blue ice as he surveyed the girl standing across the room. 'It's obvious that you're still the same stupid, spoiled brat that I married,' he remarked flatly.

'I certainly was stupid to marry you—I must have been out of my mind!'

'However, leaving aside my own extreme annoyance at your childish behaviour,' he continued, ignoring her angry protest, 'I'm afraid that you've succeeded in seriously upsetting Miss van de Burgh.'

'I—I'm sorry,' Samantha muttered, ashamed to find herself having to stifle a grin at the thought of the cool blonde's discomfort.

'I'm sure you are. And Corrine will undoubtedly expect your grovelling apology.'

'You must be joking!' she snapped. 'I've told you I'm sorry, and that's all you're going to get from me.'

'Really...?'

Cold shivers feathered down her spine as she registered the tone of grim menace underlying his lazy drawl. Remembering how, in the past, he had never given an inch in any argument or discussion, she swiftly decided that the sooner she brought this disastrous reunion to a close, the better.

'It's hardly been a pleasure—but it certainly has been interesting to meet you again, Luke. Especially since it's emphasised just how totally incompatible we always were.' She looked pointedly down at her wristwatch. 'However, it's getting late and I've got a lot of work to do, so I'm going to have to ask you to leave.'

His lips curved into a brief, wintry smile. 'No, I don't think so.'

'Who cares what you think?' she snarled, before taking a deep breath as she strove to regain her temper and assume a façade of cool composure. Her fingers itched with an imperative, urgent desire to slap that superior smile off his handsome face! 'Just in case I didn't make myself clear, maybe I'd better put it more bluntly: I want you out of here, right this minute. Beat it... vamoose... *get lost!*' she added furiously, when it became clear he was making no effort to move.

'I'll leave when I'm ready to do so, and not before,' he drawled.

'Oh—to hell with you!' she retorted, tightening the belt on her gown as she turned and stalked over to a drinks tray.

She really ought to be in the hotel kitchen by now, supervising the preparation of the evening meal. But since her bedroom up in the gallery was open to the sitting-room below, there was no way she could begin to get dressed while Luke was still here. Giving an exasperated, heavy sigh, she gazed dully down at the bottles on the tray. If she was going to have to face much more of her husband—and it very much looked as if she was—then she was definitely going to need some Dutch courage.

'If you're offering me a drink, I'll have a neat Scotch,' Luke murmured.

'I'm not offering you a damn thing,' she grated, without looking round as she concentrated on pouring herself a large, medicinal dose of rum.

His swift movement across the floor was so sudden that he caught her completely by surprise, the bottle of rum flying from her hands and landing on a nearby couch as he grasped her arm, roughly spinning her around to face him.

'What do you think you're doing?' she cried, stunned by the rapid sequence of events.

His blue eyes were glinting chips of ice, his wide mouth set and grim as he put his hands on her shoulders and shook her fiercely. 'I'm not putting up with any more of your atrocious, infantile rudeness!' he growled. 'It's about time I taught you some decent manners.'

Samantha, rapidly recovering from her shock, was now almost spitting with fury. 'Teach me manners...?' She gave a high, shrill laugh. 'Oh, yeah? You and who else...?'

Even as she uttered the childish challenge, she knew that she had made a very grave mistake. Jerked swiftly forward, she just had enough time to feel his breath on her face, to smell the distinctive male scent of tobacco and aftershave, before his arms closed about her like a vice and his furiously angry, tanned face came swiftly down towards her.

The mouth that possessed hers was hard and forceful, obliterating all coherent thought as he forced her lips apart, his tongue an instrument of savage torture as he ravaged the inner softness of her mouth in a brutal invasion that seemed endless. Unable to move, almost unable to breathe beneath his emotional assault, she was almost fainting when he at last relaxed the cruel pressure, slowly raising his dark head to stare intently down at the girl lying like a broken doll in his arms.

'That . . . that hurt!' she gasped, her eyes swimming with tears of helpless rage and self-pity.

Luke's face was drawn and pale beneath his tan, a muscle beating in his clenched jaw as he gazed into eyes which resembled large, tragic pools of shimmering emerald. 'It was meant to!' he rasped, before his taut features gradually relaxed and he gave a heavy sigh. 'You should have known better than to deliberately provoke me, Samantha.'

'I . . . I didn't . . .'

'Oh, yes, indeed you did,' he murmured, raising a hand to gently brush away the damp hair from her brow. 'The only question is—why? Perhaps we should try to discover the answer, hmm?'

Shattered and bemused by his onslaught, it was a second or two before his words broke through the confusion in her brain. *'No . . . !'* she shrieked, her cry abruptly terminated as once again his mouth claimed her lips.

She fought him with all the dwindling reserves of strength at her command, beating her fists against his broad shoulders and any other part of his anatomy that she could reach. It was a fruitless, humiliating exercise as he adroitly captured her wrists with contemptuous ease, using one of his large hands to clasp them behind her back, while burying his other hand in the tangled mass of her fiery red hair.

Totally exhausted by the futile protest which had claimed every ounce of her strength, she slowly realised that the mouth possessing hers was not, as she had feared, a hard, brutal instrument of torture. Instead of the punishing pressure, his lips were soft and tender as they moved sensuously over hers, arousing a response she was unable to control as a treacherous warmth invaded her trembling limbs.

The sweet seduction of his lips and tongue, together with her close, intimate contact with the hard male contours of his body was having a disastrous effect on her long-dormant emotions. Despite all that had been wrong with their marriage, the sexual chemistry between them had always been a strong, powerful force in their relationship, and she wasn't too bemused not to know that Luke was using the one weapon which had never failed him. But it was four long years since a man had held her like this, and his deepening kiss was tearing down all her carefully erected barriers, leaving her helpless to prevent her body from responding to the rising tide of passion racing through her veins.

Releasing her wrists, his hand moved slowly down over her spine, sliding sinuously over the thin silk gown as he erotically traced the warm curves of her body, before slipping it off her shoulder to expose the burgeoning fullness of her breast. She shivered with delight at the sensual, erotic touch of his fingers on her soft flesh, a moan breaking from her throat as his lips left hers to gently kiss away the teardrops trembling on her damp eyelashes, and then trailing a slow, scorching path on down over her neck and throat before fastening possessively over the swollen peak of her breast.

Trapped in a dense mist of desire and pleasure, it was some moments before Samantha realised that the buzzing sound in her ears was coming from the telephone on her desk by the window.

'Ignore it,' Luke muttered impatiently as she began to struggle for release from his embrace. But the enchanted, magic spell which he had woven was now shattered to smithereens, and with a sob she tore herself out of his arms. Her hands shaking as if she was in the grip of a fever, she frantically clutched her gown together and retied her sash, fighting to control her ragged breathing as she stared at him in horrified consternation.

What on earth had she been doing? This was Luke Brandon—her dreaded husband—and a man for whom she was quite, *quite* certain that she felt nothing but acute dislike, if not downright hatred!

The phone finally stopped ringing, but neither of them noticed the fact. Luke's face was pale, his eyes glittering like icicles. He, too, seemed to be breathing unsteadily, but he had no apparent difficulty in finding his voice.

'Despite your assurance to the contrary, it would seem that we're not *totally* incompatible, after all,' he drawled.

'Oh, yes, we are!' she assured him grimly. 'What . . . well, what happened, just now, doesn't mean a damn thing. It's just . . .' She waved her hands distractedly in the air. 'It's just—er—some sort of physical chemistry, that's all. Believe me,' she added huskily, 'the days when you pulled the sexual strings and I danced to your tune are well and truly over.'

'Not from where I was standing!' He gave her a cold, mocking smile. 'You may not wear my wedding ring any longer, but you wanted me just now, and there's little point in denying it.'

She could feel her cheeks flaming at the flat, hard certainty in his voice. God—he really was the pits! Anyone, with even half an ounce of sensitivity in his veins, would surely see that there was nothing to be gained in raking over the ashes of a dead relationship.

'Luke, please do try to be reasonable,' she said as calmly as she could. 'You can't just walk casually back into my life like this.'

'Why not? You walked just as casually out of mine.'

'Oh, no, I didn't! I ran—as fast and as far as my legs would carry me!'

There was a long silence as Samantha gazed at the hard, impassive expression on his face, which gave no clue to what he was thinking. 'OK,' she said at last. 'Maybe I should have stayed in New York, found myself a smart lawyer and gone for a quick divorce. Perhaps it was childish and juvenile to take to my heels and run away.' She sighed, brushing a trembling hand through the tangled curls of her long red hair. 'But that was four years ago, Luke, and I'm no longer the young girl you married. Maybe you remember her: that pathetically naïve, unsophisticated eighteen-year-old...?' she added bitterly. 'Well, things are very different now. I know what I want out of life.'

He surveyed her with cool detachment. 'And just what *do* you want, Samantha?'

'A lot of things you wouldn't even begin to appreciate,' she retorted sharply, stung by his patronising attitude and the clear note of ironic scepticism in his deep voice. 'However, first and foremost I want a divorce!'

'Why?'

'"Why?"' she echoed blankly, looking at him in astonishment. 'For heaven's sake—surely it must be obvious? After all, we've been separated for so long...both of us living separate lives, and...'

'Are you planning to marry someone else?'

She cursed inwardly as she felt her cheeks redden beneath the narrowing gaze from his piercing blue eyes. No, she wasn't—not at the moment, anyway—although she had no intention of telling him so. Besides, he had a nerve questioning her about her future matrimonial plans—especially since he was the one who was travelling around the Caribbean with a flashy blonde girlfriend in tow!

'Well?'

'If... well, if I am thinking of getting married again, it has absolutely nothing to do with you,' she said firmly.

'Oh, no?' Luke gave a harsh bark of sardonic laughter as he spun on his heels and strode over towards the door. 'If you want my consent to a divorce, I think you'll find that—as your present husband—it has *everything* to do with me!'

A moment later he was gone. Samantha stood rooted to the spot, so shaken by his abrupt departure that it was some time before the sweet smell of rum drew her attention to the bottle which had fallen on to the couch. Wrinkling her nose at the strong aroma, she removed the damp cushions and cleared up the mess, before forcing her trembling legs to climb the stairs to the gallery bedroom, where she lay down and stared blindly up at the ceiling.

Damn, damn and double damn! She'd really made a mess of things just now, hadn't she? Instead of demonstrating to Luke that she was no longer the immature, emotional young girl to whom he had once been married, she had been so thrown by his sudden arrival that she'd completely lost both her cool, and her temper. She hadn't *ever* wanted to see him again, of course. But if and when they eventually met, she had been fully determined to impress upon Luke the fact that she was now a grown woman and, if not exactly dripping with poise and sang-froid, at least quite capable of being calm and collected in the face of adversity. And if 'the face of adversity' wasn't a perfect, apposite description of his unexpected reappearance in her life, she didn't know what was!

So he'd materialised in her life at long last, and what had happened? She'd blown it—that was what had happened! It seemed almost unbelievable to realise that it had taken her less than five minutes to casually toss aside any wisdom and maturity she had gained over the last four years. In truth, she had no option but to face the degrading fact that Luke had, as always, made mincemeat of her. Despite not having set eyes on the dreadful man for so long, it seemed that the moment he hove into view, all her composure and finesse disappeared into thin air.

And it wasn't just their verbal sparring which had left her feeling so shattered. Samantha writhed with shame and self-disgust as she recalled her totally uninhibited response when she had found herself clasped in his arms. Admittedly, she hadn't welcomed his first, determined assault. But she hadn't exactly been screaming and shouting during his subsequent embrace, had she? Even now, her body still felt as if it was at a feverish temperature of white heat, throbbing with unconsummated pleasure and thwarted desire; her senses clamouring for release from the excitement engendered by the feel of his warm hands on her bare flesh, the erotic caress of his mouth and tongue on her breasts...

'*No*...! I won't think about it—*I won't!*' she shouted up at the rafters, before hurriedly scrambling off the bed and dashing over to pull open the door of her wardrobe. She must...she really must get changed. Any minute now the staff would be starting to serve dinner in the hotel. Frantically, her trembling hands sorted through her few simple evening dresses, and after a moment's indecision she decided upon a plain black silk frock. The colour definitely reflected her mood, she thought gloomily as she sat down at her dressing-table, struggling to bring some sort of order to her dishevelled, curly hair.

'You're going to have to get a grip on yourself—and fast!'—she told her reflection, pausing for a moment to stare at the hectic flush staining her pale cheeks, and the glittering shimmer in the depths of her emerald eyes. Oh, lord! Luke, as usual, had been quite right. She did...had...wanted him to make love to her. To her horror a deep tide of crimson flooded over her face as she recognised the ache deep in her stomach, acknowledged the reason why her legs felt like cotton wool, and her fingers were trembling so badly. She had been so certain, so confident, after all this time, that Luke's strong physical presence would no longer have the power to excite or disturb her. A heavy black lump of despair and misery seemed to settle on her heart as she realised just how wrong she had been.

Tormented by the knowledge of her own weakness, she let her eyes slide away from the all-too-revealing image in the mirror. There was only one certain, sure answer to the problem. She must get away from the hotel, and the island, just as soon as she possibly could manage to do so.

Samantha gave a heavy sigh and leaned back in her chair, massaging the tired muscles at the back of her neck. It was hopeless. She'd been sitting here in the office for the past hour, desperately trying to concentrate on the hotel's account with a wine merchant on the nearby island of St Barthélemy, but the figures simply didn't make any sense. She was just deciding that her inability to come to a correct balance was clearly due to Luke's

unexpected appearance and her consequently distraught
frame of mind, rather than the wine merchant's du-
plicity, when there was a knock and Penny Bird popped
her head around the door.

'I thought I'd let you know that the girls are just
serving the dessert,' Penny said, her cheerful smile fading
as she looked closer at Samantha's weary figure. 'Are
you all right?'

'Yes, I'm fine—just a bit tired, that's all. How's it
going?'

'No problems, except that Thomas must have been
well and truly hung-over this morning. I don't know what
else he put into the chilled chicken and tomato con-
sommé, but he certainly overdid the garlic!' she laughed.

Samantha groaned. 'Oh, no! Have there been many
complaints?'

'Luckily, no one seems to have noticed—and as all the
guests had the soup, we might get away with it. However,
the pork was a great success. There's no doubt that when
he's sober, Thomas is a genius in the kitchen.'

'"When" being the operative word. I don't know how
my aunt managed to keep him away from the bottle, but
I don't seem to be having much success,' Samantha said,
sighing as she put the account books aside and rose to
her feet.

The other girl gazed at her with concern. 'You're
looking a bit pale. Why don't you take the rest of the
evening off? There's nothing that Lester and I can't
handle between us.'

'That's a kind offer, Penny, and I might well take you
up on it later. However, I must go and chat to the guests,
or Aunt Em will never forgive me.'

Waiting until the girl had left the office, Samantha
went into the adjoining small washroom to comb her
hair. Penny was right—she did look awful, but she really

couldn't put it off any longer. She was going to have to force herself to go into the dining-room, making the rounds of the tables and seeing that the hotel guests had no complaints. Bending forward to wash her hands, which were damp and clammy with tension, she would have given everything she possessed to be able to avoid 'the evening round' as her aunt called it. But when Aunt Emily had been carted off to hospital, it was one of the points about running the hotel on which she had been most emphatically insistent.

'It's my home,' she had said firmly. 'And I always treat the hotel guests as if they were my own private visitors. So, whatever else you do, I want you to go around the dining-room at the end of dinner and make sure that everyone's enjoyed their meal.'

It was normally no problem to comply with her aunt's request, since many of the guests were old friends, staying at the hotel year after year. Besides which, it was a perfect time, when the visitors were feeling relaxed and replete, to hear all their news: about their children's marriages and the birth of new grandchildren. While for those who were new to the island—and her aunt's somewhat eccentric style of hotel management—it was equally useful to be able to deal with any minor queries or complaints before they became major problems.

But not tonight! Dealing with the other guests was no problem, but she couldn't seem to be able to stop her legs shaking at the thought of having to face Luke and his girlfriend. It was all too reminiscent of those dreadful, business-orientated dinner parties which he had insisted on holding in that grim New York apartment, during the early days of their marriage. Young and gauche, she had been unable to cope with the superior condescension of his servants, and far too nervous and shy of the sophisticated men and women—every one of them

high achievers—to try and participate in their brilliant
and sparkling conversation. She shuddered at the
memory of the many gaffes and *faux pas* which she had
made and the patient, if increasingly exasperated tone
in which Luke had pointed out her mistakes after his
guests had left. Maybe if he had been more patient and
understanding of the unfamiliar pressures she was under,
matters might have turned out differently, but she
doubted it. Not while his personal assistant, Adele
Francis, had been around to see that any difficulty was
magnified into a major disaster, Samantha recalled bitterly. Adele, a cool, blonde career-girl, who might be
Corrine van de Burgh's twin, had made quite sure that
all Samantha's attempts to explain her problems to Luke
had ended in abject failure. And with the discovery that
Adele was not just his personal assistant, but was also
having an affair with her husband, Samantha had finally realised that her brief marriage was well and truly
over.

'Come on—snap out of it! You're twenty-three now,
and perfectly well able to cope with the tough Mr
Brandon, *and* his latest blonde girlfriend,' she told her
reflection, but the eyes staring back at her belied the
confident words. Luke was quite capable of saying or
doing anything—and after that devastating confrontation between them in the sugar mill . . . well, goodness
knew what he might say or do.

However, as much as she dreaded the forthcoming en-
counter, she really couldn't stay hiding here in the
washroom all night. If she didn't put in an appearance
very soon, Penny would be back to see if she was all
right. The fact that she was married to one of the guests
would undoubtedly leak out, sooner or later; but she
was feeling too tired and exhausted to face any expla-
nations tonight. Besides, the staff in the hotel were at

full stretch, and it was unfair of her to give them any more work to do. And, did she really want to give Luke the pleasure, and the satisfaction, of knowing that she was too disturbed by his unexpected arrival to be able to face him?

It was that last question which finally gave her the necessary courage. Taking a deep breath and squaring her shoulders, Samantha walked determinedly out of the office and along the corridor towards the dining-room.

CHAPTER THREE

THE long, rectangular dining-room was the crowning glory of the Hamilton Plantation Hotel. Conscious of the antiquity of the old plantation house, Aunt Emily had decided to recreate the atmosphere of an eighteenth-century English dining-room. The guests used knives and forks of solid silver, the glasses and decanters were of the finest crystal, and the use of electric light was completely banned; the room was illuminated only by candles, set in silver candelabra on the polished mahogany tables. Even the waitresses continued the period theme, with their floor-length dresses of sprigged muslin over which they wore long aprons and mob caps of starched organdie.

'Samantha, honey!' Mrs Finberg waved as she entered the room. 'That rum sauce with the tenderloin of pork was absolutely delicious,' the American woman said as Samantha approached the table. 'Hector says I must get hold of the recipe, by fair means or foul!'

Samantha smiled down at the elderly couple. Betty and Hector Finberg had been coming to the hotel as long as she could remember, and were among her aunt's oldest friends.

'Come off it, Betty! You know you're every bit as good a cook as Thomas—probably better, in fact,' she grinned. 'And you don't need my help to wheedle the recipe out of him—always provided he stays sober, that is.'

'Oh, dear. Smashed again, is he?' Betty gave her a sympathetic smile. 'I don't suppose that's making your life any easier.'

'You're dead right! However, I'm trying to keep that fact from both the other guests and Aunt Em,' she said in a lower tone of voice. 'In fact, I'm only telling *you*, because I have a dreadful premonition that I'm going to find myself stuck in the kitchen, having to take over the cooking if he goes seriously off the wagon. And then I'll need all the advice and help I can get!'

'No problem,' the elderly woman assured her. 'I've never cooked for a hotel full of guests, so I guess it could be a lot of fun. By the way, how was Emily when you visited her today? Giving everyone hell?'

'Need you ask...?' Samantha gave a rueful laugh, and, promising the elderly couple that she'd have a long talk with them tomorrow, she continued her circuit of the dining-room.

On first entering the room, she had immediately spotted the elegantly dressed couple dining on their own, and although she had left them till last, she was eventually forced to approach their table. Taking a deep breath to steady her nerves, Samantha tried to stifle her envy of the blonde girl's glamorous silk creation, and her peaches and cream complexion and classical profile—so totally at variance with her own plain black dress, tumbling red curls and freckles. Ignoring Luke, she asked his girlfriend if she had enjoyed the meal.

'Yes, it was very nice,' the girl drawled with a marked lack of enthusiasm. 'However, I'm not quite sure...?' She peered down at her plate.

'Corinne is puzzled about the identity of the main ingredient in the dessert,' Luke's deep tones were heavy with sardonic amusement. 'But I'm sure you'll be able to enlighten us...?'

Ha, ha! Very funny! Samantha's green eyes flashed with anger. What a rat-fink that man was! He knew perfectly well what was in the pie—especially since it had always been one of his favourite desserts. It was obvious that Luke was just trying to get in a cheap dig at her expense—an embarrassing reminder of her foolish, momentary weakness in his arms, earlier in the evening. How *could* she have been so abysmally stupid as to respond to his kiss in the way she had? She must have been temporarily out of her mind!

'...And I believe that you also have an apology to make to Miss van de Burgh, hmm?'

Oh, no, I don't! If Luke thought she was going to apologise to his oh-so-cool girlfriend for the trouble at the airport—he had another think coming! Turning towards him, Samantha seethed with an overpowering longing to pick up the girl's custard pie, and slam it hard up against his handsome, tanned face. And if there wasn't a room full of guests paying the earth for their food and accommodation, she wouldn't have a moment's hesitation in doing so! However, under the circumstances she was going to have to find a slightly more subtle method of retaliation.

'I'm sure that Miss van de Burgh is a realistic and—er—sophisticated woman,' Samantha murmured smoothly. 'And she will therefore readily understand that many of our *elderly* guests—such as possibly you, Mr Brandon?—are apt to become a little jaded...if you know what I mean? So, on their arrival we like to give them a nice, big helping of Passion Fruit Pie. I'm told that...'

'That's quite enough, Samantha!' Luke grated harshly.

'Oh, dear, I was just getting to the really interesting bit!' she said, her lips curving into a broad, malicious smile.

'Strange as it may seem, I think we can do without the "interesting bit",' he said grimly, although Samantha was astonished to see a slight twitch at the corner of his mouth.

'In that case, I'll leave you to enjoy the rest of the meal,' she murmured, trying not to grin as she noted the stunned expression on Corrine's face.

Samantha turned quickly on her heel and made her way out of the dining-room, a puzzled frown creasing her forehead. It wasn't possible, of course, but for one moment it had seemed as if Luke had been struggling not to laugh. But it was so extraordinarily unlikely that he could appreciate a joke against himself, that she swiftly came to the conclusion she must have been mistaken. A shared sense of humour hadn't been one of the features of their marriage. She had been far too much in awe of her husband to think of teasing him, and he had certainly never given her cause to think that he found life anything other than deadly serious. However, she didn't have time to speculate any further on the matter, as she was called to the reception desk by Penny, who needed someone to take over while she ran two of the waitresses back to their village.

Half an hour later, having cashed a cheque for one of the guests, she was just sitting back and beginning to relax, appreciating the peace and quiet of the busy hotel, only disturbed by the quiet murmur of the guests having coffee and liqueurs in the bar, when the telephone rang.

'Hello. Can I speak to Miss Ward, please?'

'Gerald . . .!' Oh, lord—she'd promised to phone him, but thanks to Luke's unexpected appearance, she'd completely forgotten all about it. 'How are you? I . . .'

'I'm fine, but where on earth have you been? I rang you late this afternoon, and the girl on reception said that you weren't in the hotel.'

'I'm sorry, Gerald, but I didn't know you'd called. I was probably in the sugar mill, and...' A shadow fell over the register in front of her, and Samantha looked up to see Luke leaning casually against the desk. Scowling at him, she turned away and tried to concentrate on what Gerald was saying.

'...rang the sugar mill, but there was no reply. What's going on?'

'Nothing...nothing is going on,' she muttered quickly, a hectic flush spreading over her face as she recalled exactly what she and Luke had been doing at the time of Gerald's phone call. 'I was—er—probably just having a shower when you rang.'

'What...? I can't hear you. Why are you whispering?'

'Well, I... Just a moment, Gerald.' She put her hand over the receiver and turned to Luke. 'Go away!' she hissed.

'Why should I?'

'Because I'm trying to have a private conversation— that's why!'

'Ah!' He paused, raising a dark eyebrow. 'And that is the boyfriend, I take it?'

'It's nothing to do with you who I'm talking to,' she retorted angrily, her fury increased by the fact that she knew her burning cheeks had already provided the answer to his question.

Turning away, she lifted the receiver to her ear. 'Hello, Gerald...? *Oh, no!* We've been cut off. And it's all your fault!' she accused Luke bitterly. 'Why couldn't you mind your own damn business?'

Luke continued to lean casually against the desk, a mocking smile on his lips. 'Well, darling, some of us elderly, *jaded* husbands—if you know what I mean...?' he murmured, giving her a wolfish leer, '...might just feel that our wives' boyfriends were *definitely* our business!'

Samantha stared at him in astonishment, completely stunned for a moment by the way he had picked up the gauntlet she had thrown down in the dining-room. Goodness! He certainly seemed to have changed from the grim, no-nonsense businessman of four years ago. And then her seething anger at what she regarded as his quite unwarranted interference in her affairs reasserted itself. What a nerve the man had! Arriving at this hotel with his girlfriend—those two separate bungalows didn't fool her, not for one minute!—and then having the impudence to think that he was in a position to object to her quite innocent friendship with Gerald. It was time she made her position quite clear. If she hadn't been in a hurry to get a divorce in the past, she was now quite firmly determined to sever all connection with her thoroughly detestable, and quite obnoxious 'ex'-husband.

'I'm sure I don't need your say-so for a divorce, and I'm going to get some legal advice as soon as possible,' she snarled. 'In fact, now I come to think about it, I reckon I've got more than enough evidence to divorce *you*!'

'What in the hell do you mean? What evidence?' he demanded.

'You know very well—so don't bother to try and play the innocent with me,' she retorted.

'I'm not trying to play anything,' he grated with angry impatience. 'I simply don't know what you're talking about.'

Samantha gave a snort of derision. 'Oh, yeah? What about your little playmate? Or are you going to try and pretend that Miss "Cool Corrine" is merely a figment of my overheated imagination?' she queried with acid contempt.

'Corrine?' Luke frowned, his hooded blue eyes searching her face for a moment before he gave a short bark of sardonic amusement. 'Well, well...'

'I couldn't care less about your girlfriend,' she assured him quickly.

'No...?' he mocked, raising a dark, quizzical eyebrow. 'Unfortunately, I'm afraid that I'm not prepared to be *quite* so understanding about *your* boyfriend,' he drawled, his voice heavy with menace.

'That's just too bad!' she snapped.

Luke leaned against the desk, a cold smile touching his mouth as he surveyed her defiant expression. 'I wonder—does your Romeo know that you're still married to me?'

She flushed. 'Our so-called marriage is a mere technicality,' she said quickly. 'And before you start threatening me, or trying to interfere in my life, I suggest that you'd better concentrate on cleaning up your own act!' she added waspishly as she spun on her heel, and stalked past him towards the front door of the hotel.

It was a hot, sticky night, and for Samantha, tossing and turning as she stared wide-eyed up at the ceiling and desperately trying to seek oblivion in sleep, it appeared to be endless. The shrill, screeching sounds of the cicadas and the little tree frogs in the long grass outside the sugar mill, so much a normal part of the background noise of a Caribbean night, now seemed to be hammering through her skull like the high-pitched whine of a dentist's drill.

Eventually giving up the unequal fight, she threw back the thin sheet which was her only covering, and, slipping on a light cotton robe, she made her way down the staircase to the small kitchen off the main room to make herself a cup of tea.

A cup of tea: the automatic response of the English when faced with moments of stress and strain—that nation's panacea for all ills! Samantha smiled wryly to herself as she spooned the tea-leaves into the pot. She was only half-English, but maybe it was at times such as the last twenty-four hours that those particular genes came to the fore. Genes and possibly environment too, of course, although there had been nothing remotely American—or English for that matter—about the freezing cold, grim castle of Kildonan in the far north of Scotland.

She had been only five years old when her parents had divorced, and her beautiful English mother, Nina Ward, had left both her husband Maurice and the United States of America to marry Sir Ian Alexander, taking her small daughter with her. Goodness knew why her mother, a frivolous and empty-headed woman who required constant stimulation and amusement, should have married a man with such a dour, morose and sullen character. Maybe, being British herself, she had been attracted by the snobbery value of her new husband's ancient baronetcy? If so, the novelty of being able to call herself Lady Alexander had very quickly worn off. Even as a very young child, Samantha had known that her mother and stepfather were completely unsuited to each other, Nina quickly becoming bored, and then progressively sour and bitter at being trapped in the grey-stoned, gloomy castle miles from what she regarded as civilisation.

Samantha, too, was not happy. Looked after by a succession of nannies—the rapid turnover being due to the remote situation of the castle, and the increasing unpredictability of her mother who had discovered the anaesthetising effect of Scotch whisky—Samantha had hated the small local village school. Teased by the other children because of her American accent, and ostracised outside school hours because of the social gulf between the inhabitants of the castle and the village, she had lived for the summer holidays, when she was allowed to join her father at the large family house in Newport, Rhode Island.

Now, of course, she could see that Maurice Ward, though a charming, well-read and erudite man, had also been weak and idle. Happy to live off the wealth he had inherited from his parents—mainly investments in oil and heavy industry—Maurice had swanned carelessly through life in the company of his equally rich and idle friends. But for Samantha, those long, hot summers had seemed bathed in a rosy glow of perfection, sharply at variance with her lonely, unhappy life in the Highlands of Scotland, and the ever-increasingly bleak antipathy which had existed between herself and her stepfather.

The unhappy state of affairs at Kildonan Castle had come to an abrupt end when she was thirteen—just as abruptly as the car crash in which Nina had killed herself. The true facts had been played down at the inquest, but Samantha had quickly become aware, from the servants' hints and gossip in the village, that her mother had been drinking heavily before the accident, being almost paralytically drunk when she had driven her vehicle into the side of a mountain.

Nina's death had heralded the arrival into Samantha's life of her hitherto unknown great-aunt, Emily, who had swept like a whirlwind through Kildonan Castle, imperiously brushing aside the tentative arrangements being discussed between Maurice Ward and Sir Ian Alexander. To the dour Scotsman's undisguised relief, she had informed both him and her nephew, Maurice, that the young girl needed friends of her own age, and quickly packed Samantha off to an English boarding-school. Emily Ward had also insisted that her great-niece should join her for the Christmas and Easter holidays on the Caribbean island of St Pauls. The long summers, when she stayed with her father at the family estate in Newport, were still very precious to Samantha; but it was her aunt, a larger-than-life, often impatient and sometimes exasperating character, whom she had come to care for so deeply. In providing the first real home life, as well as a warmth and kindness the girl had never known before, Aunt Emily had quickly gained Samantha's undying love and gratitude.

Dear Aunt Em, Samantha thought fondly as she poured herself another cup of tea. The indomitable old woman was undoubtedly disrupting the hospital, and driving her doctors to distraction! How could they know about the other side of her character, the tender care and concern she had shown for a girl so many years younger than herself? Samantha had soon come to realise, for instance, that the gruff harshness her aunt had displayed before putting her on the aeroplane to New York at the beginning of each summer holidays—'Hurry up—I haven't the time to stand here all day, you know!'—had merely been a front to disguise her feelings at the prospect of not seeing her niece for the next three months.

Unfortunately, there was no way that either of them could possibly have guessed, as they bade each other farewell at Antigua airport, the summer of Samantha's eighteenth birthday, just how long it would be before they saw each other again.

On joining her father at his home on Newport, Rhode Island, she had been shocked and horrified to find Maurice looking so drawn and ill. Resolutely denying that there was anything wrong with his health, he had insisted that now she was grown up, she must participate in all the local social events. And thus it was that Samantha found herself entering a life that was fraught with hitherto unknown difficulties. Late to mature, she was at last emerging from her chrysalis, changing from a gawky teenager to find herself standing on the threshold of full-blown womanhood. But her relatively monastic state at a boarding-school for girls, and her brief holidays on a small Caribbean island with her maiden aunt, hadn't prepared Samantha in any way for the adult society in such a sophisticated resort. Confused and bewildered by the admiration and often unwelcome attentions of strange men—not to mention the boys whom she'd known all her life, and who were now acting towards her in a most peculiar and thoroughly sloppy manner—Samantha was delighted to meet a girl of her own age living next door.

The estate adjoining her father's had recently been bought by a millionaire business tycoon, principally for the use of his widowed mother and much younger sister. It was some time before Samantha had met the owner, but she and Barbara Brandon had quickly become good friends. They would spend hours trying on each other's clothes, experimenting with make-up, and discussing the totally absorbing topic of their future relationships with the male sex. Barbara too, it seemed, had been brought up under strict supervision.

'Luke used to be such fun, but he's a real pain these days,' Barbara had complained about her elder brother. 'I mean, he's so old—at least thirty and really ancient!— and he's obviously forgotten what it's like to be young. Every time he comes down here, he puts me through the third degree,' she added with a scowl. 'He wants to know where I've been and who I've met—it's a real drag!'

'How awful,' Samantha had murmured sympathetically as she tried one of the other girl's new lipsticks.

'Mom says that he acts the heavy brother because, since Dad died, Luke feels he has to keep a fatherly eye on me,' Barbara explained, busily padding out her bra with tissues. 'Still, at least he's agreed to let me go off next week, with my old schoolfriend Jennifer, to stay with her grandparents in London.' She turned around. 'OK. How do I look?'

'Well...' Samantha gazed at her friend doubtfully.

'You're right—I never really thought it would work, anyway,' Barbara muttered, gloomily regarding her lack of curves in the mirror. 'I'm sick to death of being so flat-chested! You just don't know how lucky you are to have such a tiny waist and large boobs—and you're a lot prettier than some of those New York girls that Luke brings down here. Hey—I've just had a fantastic idea!' she added enthusiastically. 'Luke's coming to stay with mother in a few days' time. Wouldn't it be neat if he decided to take a shine to you?'

'Oh, no, I don't really think...' Samantha had blushed, and changed the subject. She hadn't wanted to upset her new friend, but the idea of getting involved with a man who must be at least twelve years older than she was definitely sounded a fate worse than death!

However, fate, in the guise of an over-frisky horse, had intervened only a week later. Lying stunned on the ground as her mount cantered off back home to his stable, she had been rescued by a stranger who had also decided to go riding before breakfast.

With dazed eyes she had blinked up at the tall figure outlined against the hazy mist of the early morning sun, and to her bewildered mind it appeared as though the man astride the huge black stallion was the reincarnation of some romantic, medieval knight. Time seemed to be suspended as they stared silently at one another, the stranger's brilliant blue eyes absorbing the sight of the girl's slim body lying on the grass, her pale face framed by the fiery tresses of her long, curly hair. And then the enchanted spell was broken as his dark horse restlessly pawed the ground. Quickly leaping down from the saddle, he had moved swiftly to where she lay, placing his arms about her as he helped her to sit up. Once he had established the fact that she hadn't broken her leg, as she had at first thought, but had only twisted her ankle, he had asked for her name and address.

'There's really no need for you to bother...' she had murmured breathlessly as he swept her up in his strong arms, taking no notice of her mild protest as he lifted her gently on to his horse.

'It's no bother. After all—it isn't every day that I get the opportunity to rescue a fair damsel in distress!' he'd drawled, the amusement in his voice sharply at variance with the hard, determined glint in the eyes regarding her so fixedly.

The sound of his rich, dark voice and the strength of the bare, tanned forearms as he gathered up the reins before swinging himself up on the saddle behind her, had seemed to be having the most peculiar effect on both her breathing and her pulse-rate. Still shocked and disorientated from her fall, she had been unable to completely cast aside her original vision: it's just like...like Guinevere being rescued by Lancelot, she had thought, her senses bemused by the warmth of the body pressed so close to her own as they rode slowly and silently back to her home.

'Ah, there you are—I was getting anxious,' her father had exclaimed as they reached Maurice Ward's mansion, and it was only when the tall stranger had lifted her down and then introduced himself that she discovered her rescuer to be none other than Luke Brandon. Astonished and confused, it was some moments before she had managed to fully comprehend that—far from being a wrinkled, ancient geriatric—Barbara's brother was a quite extraordinarily good-looking, and rivetingly attractive man!

Her father had warmly welcomed Luke into the house, and during the weeks that followed the two men had become very friendly, with the younger man coming over to spend long hours with Maurice and his daughter. As for Samantha, she was dazed and fascinated by their handsome neighbour, and as the days passed she had known that she was, for the first time in her life, deeply in love. Other than a brief, mad infatuation for one of the guests at her great-aunt's hotel, she had never been in love before; but she had absolutely no doubt that what she felt for this tall, dark and overwhelmingly sophisticated man was absolutely *the real thing*.

It was the sort of love about which she had always dreamed, the highly charged, emotional intensity which pervaded her favourite book, *Wuthering Heights*: wild, exhilarating and completely intoxicating. Not that she had ever intended to do anything about her feelings for Luke. He was so much older, and with his obviously vast experience of life—and women—she had known that she must appear to be no more than a child in his eyes. In fact, she was so totally consumed by her secret, hopeless passion that apart from daydreaming for hours about how she would rescue her beloved from various dire accidents—which he would reward with a chaste kiss on her brow—she was content to worship from afar. Of course, if Barbara hadn't been away in England, or if she had been able to talk about her feelings with her father, possibly a breath of fresh air might have dissolved some of her more overheated, romantic fantasies. But Maurice was by now clearly a very sick man, and when he died in his sleep the night before he was due to go into hospital for an operation, Samantha was completely devastated.

'What's going to happen to me? What am I going to do...?' she had cried helplessly after the funeral, when she discovered that not only had she lost her beloved father, but that he had died leaving a mountainous pile of debts. Suddenly, from having been the pampered only child of a wealthy, charming and indulgent man, she had found herself virtually penniless, with the estate, house and furniture having to be quickly sold to pay Maurice's many creditors. Samantha wasn't interested in money for its own sake but, still reeling from the shocking loss of her father, she was dazed and frightened at the prospect of her uncertain future in an alien, cruel world about which she knew less than nothing.

Luke, who had been a tower of strength throughout, making all the arrangements necessary at such a difficult and desperately unhappy time, had provided the answer: 'You're going to marry me and live happily ever after.' And Samantha, stunned by the speed of events, and thrilled by Luke's assurance that he had fallen madly in love with her, from the very first moment they had met, had been blithely content to place her future in his hands.

Following their quiet, simple wedding, Luke had taken her to Boston where he had some business to conduct, before leaving for a honeymoon in Europe. Immersed in a haze of euphoric happiness, it wasn't until Samantha found herself standing in her nightdress in the vast, palatial bedroom of a huge suite at the Ritz-Carlton hotel that various doubts and uncertainties began to cloud her mind. Luke's maturity and sophistication, which she had found so attractive and reassuring, was now a cause of considerable anxiety. If only she knew what she was supposed to do now. What was her new husband going to think of someone who had never had any real, first-hand experience of an intimate, sexual relationship...?

Entering the room, clothed in a towelling robe with his hair damp from the shower, Luke had correctly interpreted the reason behind her nervous glance and rigidly taut figure. 'There's no need to be frightened of me, sweetheart,' he murmured, drawing her gently into his arms. 'I love you, and I'd never do anything to hurt you,' he added softly, slowly lowering his head until his mouth touched hers. As his embrace tightened about her slim figure, the exquisite warmth of his lips moving over hers, lingering and exploring, sent delicious thrills of desire coursing through her veins.

Dizzy with pleasure, she wound her arms about his neck and pressed her body closer to him as his kiss deepened; responding instinctively to the skilled seduction of his mouth and tongue, to the featherlight touch of his hands as they softly caressed her trembling body.

In a daze of ever-increasing passion, she barely noticed as he picked her up and carried her over to the bed. Her entire being seemed to be firmly in the grip of a feverish, shuddering excitement. She was aware of him gently removing her silk nightgown, and was suddenly glad to be free of it, astonished to find herself revelling in his softly whispered murmurs of delight, the fierce glitter in his eyes as he gazed at her body, before first his fingers and then his lips began tracing patterns of fire on her quivering flesh.

Why hadn't she known it would be like this? she wondered hazily, and then his hands cupped the aching fullness of her breasts, his mouth capturing first one hardened peak and then the other, producing a deep throbbing ache which obliterated everything except the compulsive, driving need for his total possession. It wasn't until she was almost delirious, sobbing with pleasure and groaning his name as she writhed helplessly beneath his intimate touch, that he moved to cover her body with his own. There was a sudden, brief, shocking moment of pain as her flesh yielded to his maleness, and then she was caught up in a vortex of spiralling excitement produced by the hard, pulsing rhythm, until the world seemed to explode into an amazing fireburst of sensations, her body racked by shuddering convulsions of a pleasure so intense that it was almost too much to bear.

Later, as she lay sleepily enfolded in his arms, she felt him stir. 'I hope I didn't hurt you too much, sweetheart?' he whispered, gently brushing the damp curls from her brow.

'No...not really...' She felt a hot flush creep over her face. 'I didn't realise...I mean...' She took a deep breath. 'Oh, Luke—it was *so* fantastic, *so* wonderful! Is it always like this, for everyone?'

'No, unfortunately it isn't,' he murmured huskily, gently stroking her soft, yielding flesh. 'But for you and I...yes, I think it always will be like this.'

And he was right. Their honeymoon had been a halcyon period of emotional bliss and euphoric happiness. Luke had been infinitely patient and gentle, skilfully leading her to further erotic, rapturous delights of sexual fulfilment. Beneath his skilful tuition, she had learned to discard all virginal inhibitions, to wantonly respond and delight in their mutual passion.

Now, with the benefit of five years' hindsight, Samantha nearly groaned aloud as she looked back at the innocent naïveté of her younger self. How could she have thought that a good sexual relationship with her husband was all that was required for a successful marriage? In taking the easy way out of her difficulties, by choosing the soft option of marriage to Luke, she had thrown away the opportunity to grow up and learn to stand on her own two feet. It wasn't until she had left her husband, and could bring some measure of calm objectivity to their troubled relationship, that she realised that in marrying Luke she had made the classic, fatal error of exchanging one authoritative father-figure for another.

She could recall the brief, short months of her married life as clearly and vividly as if it had been yesterday. All too soon, it seemed, they had returned from their honeymoon, and she had faced the long, empty days in Luke's large, grimly austere New York apartment. Totally absorbed in his business affairs, he had appeared to have less and less time for his young wife, although he had resolutely refused to allow her to occupy herself with any worthwhile occupation. She could still remember, with a shudder, the cataclysmic row which had followed upon Luke's discovery that she had found herself a part-time job.

'I am not prepared to discuss the matter,' he had said, curtly dismissing her reasoned arguments. 'As my wife, you are merely required to look beautiful, and to be waiting in the apartment when I come home.'

Unfortunately, and increasingly as the months went by, he often didn't come home, preferring to spend the night in his office when there was a big business deal in the offing. Neither did he telephone or feel the need to explain and apologise for his absence. When she protested, as she frequently did, he had replied with cold, brutal logic, 'I am a businessman. You must just learn to put up with it.' But she never did. And how could she, when he spent more and more time with his personal assistant, Adele Francis? Adele, a tall, cool blonde, who was not only clever, but who was also extremely beautiful, seemed to possess all the attributes that Samantha so clearly lacked. Was it any wonder that she, young, bewildered and becoming daily more and more unsure of herself, had come to believe that Luke had married her more out of a sense of pity for her situation than love? Especially when Adele was so obviously the sort of woman who was ideally suited to be the wife of a millionaire businessman. And Adele had clearly agreed with Samantha's view of the situation, treating the younger girl with cool contempt and, as time passed, being quite frank and open about the fact that she was also having an affair with her employer.

Increasingly, it had seemed that the only times she and Luke shared together were those when he slid into bed at night, and would become once again the demanding, passionate lover that she had married. But even that last refuge of their relationship began to crumble beneath her mounting resentment of being treated like a child during the day and a sex-object at night. She was too young and inexperienced to know how to combat the situation, only slowly recognising that the all-too-brief enchantment of their first months of ecstatic, wedded bliss had given way to wretched misery and despair, before finally dissolving into animosity and raw hatred.

In a last-ditch attempt to save her marriage, she had suddenly issued an ultimatum. If Luke was intending to take his personal assistant on a week's business trip to South America, then as far as she was concerned their marriage was finished. Luke had barely listened to her, brushing aside her objections to Adele as infantile and not worthy of discussion. And when, accompanied by Adele, he kept to his schedule and flew down to Rio de Janeiro, she had come to her senses at last. Realising that in marrying Luke she had made a terrible mistake,

Samantha had simply walked out of the apartment she hated so much, and fled back to the sanctuary of St Pauls and her beloved Aunt Emily. She had never been in any doubt that she had made the right decision, and since Luke had never bothered to contact her, he had clearly come to the same conclusion. In fact, for the first year or two, she had expected to hear from him asking for a divorce, so that he could marry Adele. When he had remained silent, she had assumed that he was content with his semi-bachelor life and his on-going affair with his personal assistant. She didn't know about his present relationship with Adele, but with the arrival of Luke and Corrine—another cool blonde in the same mould as Adele—it seemed as if her supposition had been correct.

Perhaps that was the basic problem, she told herself wearily as she emptied the teapot into the sink. Maybe marriage wasn't Luke's forte? It was obvious that he had bitterly regretted the impulse which had led him to marry such a young girl—possibly the only rash decision of his life. Luke evidently preferred the ruthless world of business to that of domesticity; the choice of emotional freedom rather than settled commitment. And who could blame him after the débâcle of their brief relationship? Samantha thought grimly. She, herself, had been extremely wary of any emotional entanglements during the past four years, and fond as she was of Gerald, she had steadfastly refused all his proposals of marriage. So, maybe both Luke and she really did have something in common, after all...?

CHAPTER FOUR

SAMANTHA woke up the following morning feeling tired and morose, her heavy depression aggravated by a headache, which began throbbing as soon as she lifted her head from the pillow. After stumbling over a stray shoe on the floor, and stubbing her toe on the hard base of her large, antique mahogany bed, she limped painfully downstairs in a thoroughly bad temper.

Her grouchy frame of mind was not helped by the realisation that if the events of yesterday had been traumatic—and heaven knew, they certainly had!—today didn't look like being any better. Apart from her own personal predicament, embodied by the unexpected arrival of Luke and his girlfriend, there were all the usual difficulties in trying to run the hotel.

What a life! As far as she was concerned, it was a real can of worms. If it wasn't the guests being difficult—and there seemed to be nothing and no one more demanding, and wearisome, than clients who had paid for an expensive holiday and weren't enjoying themselves—then it was the hotel staff. She had been amazed at the rapid turnover of personnel in the hotel trade; none of them seeming to stay more than five minutes in any one establishment. She was swiftly coming to think of the staffing problems as some sort of mad, frantic game of musical chairs.

And if that dipsomaniac chef, Thomas, isn't stone-cold sober today—I'll kill him! she thought grimly, hunting through the kitchen cupboard for some aspirins to alleviate the pounding in her head, which seemed to be getting worse every passing minute. It was probably due to the weather, she thought, gazing out at a sky which was unusually grey and overcast. Although the temperature was as hot as ever, it seemed far more humid than usual, the thin muslin nightgown sticking uncomfortably to her damp, moist skin. Maybe a quick dip in the sea would help to get rid of her headache, and freshen her up for the undoubtedly arduous day ahead?

Back up in the bedroom, she was just slipping into her bikini when she saw a crested hummingbird outside the open window. Always fascinated by the tiny, brilliantly coloured birds, she went over to watch it hovering, wings beating almost in a blur, as it extracted honey from the bright red flowers on the shrub climbing up the outside wall of the sugar mill. Raising her eyes to look out over the lawns leading down to the fine, sandy beach which edged the blue Caribbean sea, Samantha swore violently under her breath.

It really wasn't going to be her day! Of course, there was no logical reason why she shouldn't continue with her plans for a cooling dip in the ocean. She often joined those guests who liked to have an early-morning swim before breakfast. However, not only was the sledgehammer still pounding in her head, but it was *definitely* far too early in the day for her to feel up to coping with her husband!

Unfortunately, there was no possibility of a mistake. Even at this distance she couldn't fail to recognise Luke's tall figure, clothed only in a pair of navy blue swimming trunks, with a white towel slung over one of his broad shoulders, nor his distinctive stride as he moved lithely down over the soft sand towards the water's edge. And neither did she need twenty-twenty vision to identify the slim figure walking beside him—Miss 'Cool' van de Burgh herself. Who else?

Samantha's soft lips tightened as she viewed her husband's companion, her eyes flashing with icy green fire as they swept over the American girl. It was absolutely sickening! No one had the right to look so sensational in a one-piece bathing suit, which also somehow seemed to be far more revealing than the bikini that she herself was wearing. And telling herself that Corrine's figure was definitely on the skinny side—almost verging on scrawny, in fact—didn't seem to help at all.

Turning away from the window to gaze at her reflection in a full-length mirror, Samantha frowned as she stared critically at her own body. Although she'd always thought of herself as slim, there was no doubt that, compared to the other girl, she appeared to be positively fat. And there wasn't a damn thing she could do about it, she thought gloomily, regarding the full, generous curves of her own breasts with glum dissatisfaction. Still, at least her flesh was taut and firm, and Luke had always said...

Oh, no! She gritted her teeth, almost groaning aloud with dismay. She really *must* stop this nonsense. There was absolutely no point in remembering the past: the haunting recollections of her husband's warm, passionate endearments, or the delight he had taken in her body during their brief marriage. Those days were well and truly gone beyond recall, and the sooner they were finally banished from her treacherous memory, the better.

Quickly stripping off her bikini, she went to have a brief shower before putting on a simple, light blue cotton sundress and matching blue sandals, ready for yet another hard-working day.

'Hi, Penny, how's it going?'

The young manageress gave her a smile and a wave from the end of the kitchen as she continued to count the trays on the table. '...seven, eight, nine. That's it,' she murmured, handing a clipboard to one of the two local girls who worked in the kitchen, and were busy putting fresh toast and orange juice on to the trays. 'Everything seems to be under control,' Penny said as she came over to join Samantha. 'They've almost finished serving in the dining-room, and there are only these trays to be taken to the guests wanting a late breakfast in their bungalows.'

'Well, it sounds as though we're getting off to a good start today, thank heavens!' Samantha grinned. 'What's on the menu for lunch?'

'I'm not sure. I haven't seen Thomas this morning.'

'Oh-oh. I thought things were too good to last.'

Penny gave her a reassuring smile. 'I expect he's around here somewhere. It's only just after nine o'clock, after all.'

'He'd better put in an appearance soon,' Samantha warned her, becoming sharply conscious of the fact that the aspirins she had taken for her headache didn't seem to be working. 'Because, quite frankly, I've had just about as much as I can stand from our temperamental chef.'

'I'm sure he'll be OK.' The other girl frowned. 'I've never known him to get drunk twice in a week before.'

Samantha gave a heavy sigh. 'I only wish I could rely on that comforting fact. Still, this place is pretty dreadful, isn't it? Maybe if I had to work down here all the time, I'd take to the bottle, too.'

She glanced around at the dimly lit, subterranean kitchen which had been formed from the old cellars of the plantation house. The only daylight came from small windows set up high on the stone walls. The heat of the stoves together with the damp, muggy atmosphere, and the noisy pounding of the ancient generator which ran both the large ice machine and the refrigerators, made it seem strangely like the boiler room of an ancient, old-fashioned steamship.

'Your aunt has promised that we will soon have a new kitchen,' Penny said brightly.

'Hmm.' After having spent a great deal of time going over the hotel's books, Samantha knew very well that, far from building a new kitchen, her aunt was going to have an uphill struggle to even pay next month's wages. However, there seemed little point in curbing the girl's optimism. After all, miracles had been known to happen, although what anyone could hope to do about this hot, steaming kitchen, she had no idea. It was still early in the morning, but she was already beginning to feel sticky and uncomfortable, despite the fact that she was wearing nothing beneath the strapless, cotton top of her sundress.

'Well, if you've got everything under control, Penny, I'm just going to check today's arrivals and departures. Then, if you need me, I'll probably be out in the garden with Jason.'

An hour later, Samantha was conferring with the head gardener, who seemed strangely reluctant to do as she asked.

'Look, Jason,' she said patiently for the third time. 'I know that we have to be careful with our supply of fresh water. But it's getting hotter every day, and if we don't give the flowers and shrubs enough water, they'll die. So, get on with it, huh?'

'There ain't no point,' he said stubbornly. 'The Christmas Winds is coming very soon.'

God give me patience! she thought, staring at the mulish expression on his dark face. Everyone who lived on St Pauls knew all about the 'Christmas Winds'—the north-east trade winds which normally blew throughout December, bringing sudden rain-showers which were over almost as soon as they started. They were essential for the successful cultivation of fruit and vegetables on the island, and the main reason why the cattle pastures were so lush and green.

'It's only November, for heaven's sake,' she said, trying not to sound too exasperated. 'There's another month to go before the rains arrive—and if we wait that long, it will be too late. We can't have the grounds of this hotel looking a mess, can we?' She gestured helplessly towards a clump of drooping, red poinsettias.

'That isn't my fault,' Jason said firmly, and Samantha was forced to agree with him. Aunt Emily's attempt to establish a small, Italian-style garden, here on St Pauls, had been the least successful of her many projects.

Set at the side of the large lawn, the tall, six-foot-high dark hedges enclosing the small beds had effectively cut the sunlight from the flowers and shrubs, and the claustrophobic atmosphere of what appeared to be more of a maze than a garden was not one that the guests found attractive. Samantha had often thought that her aunt should have bulldozed it all down and built a swimming pool in its place—a suggestion which had not been well received by the formidable Emily Ward.

'I feel it in my bones that there's a storm coming soon,' the old gardener said stubbornly. 'For certain sure.'

Samantha was just opening her mouth to tell Jason to forget his bones, and to get on with the watering, when she recalled her conversation yesterday with the mechanic at Antigua airport.

'You don't mean...you haven't heard anything about Hurricane Hannah coming our way? It's supposed to be well out in the Atlantic.'

Jason shrugged. 'I ain't saying anything about a hurricane. But what I is saying is that we sure has a storm of some kind on the way.' He glanced up at the overcast sky. 'And then I reckon we'll soon have more rain than we knows what to do with.'

'All right, Jason, we'll leave it for the moment,' Samantha sighed, conceding defeat. 'In the meantime, can you and the boys see about cutting down some of the ripe coconuts? Especially from the palm trees near the bungalows. Apparently one fell down yesterday only inches away from young Zachary Dillman, and while I couldn't help wishing it might have landed on his horrid little head, I think we'd better make sure it doesn't happen again,' she grinned.

'Yes, ma'am!' The old man wheezed with laughter as he picked up the handles of his wheelbarrow and began trundling it away. 'That boy sure need a good belting from his pa.'

'*My sentiments exactly!*

Samantha nearly jumped out of her skin as she recognised the harsh, dark voice coming unexpectedly from behind her shoulder. Quickly spinning on her heel, she turned to face Luke's tall figure, clothed in a pair of brief white shorts topped by a short-sleeved, white cotton shirt. Startled and confused by his sudden appearance, she found herself staring, mesmerised, at the long length of his deeply tanned legs for some moments, before she realised that her husband was simmering with anger.

'I thought this hotel didn't take children,' he growled.

'It doesn't—well, not under the age of seven, that is,' she muttered, striving to pull herself together. 'What's the problem?'

'Oh, I wouldn't say there's a problem,' he drawled sarcastically. 'Or not one that I couldn't solve by strangling that kid with my bare hands!'

Samantha sighed as Luke paced up and down the small, narrow path, fulminating about parents who couldn't control their spoilt brats, and who insisted on inflicting them upon unsuspecting members of the general public. And after suffering from the dreaded Zachary Dillman for the past week, she found herself in strong agreement with Luke's views.

Mr and Mrs Dillman were a quiet Canadian couple who seemed strangely protective of their eight-year-old son, it never occurring to them that the trail of damage which followed Zachary's progress could in any way be due to the boy's fiendish talent for causing mayhem. Some of his pranks were harmless, of course, but she had been furious a few nights ago when he had deliberately put a dime into a lamp socket in his parents' bungalow, before replacing the light bulb. The memory of the sudden blackout during the middle of dinner, a horrendous mixture of screaming panic, wild alarm and confusion, was still capable of making her break out into a cold sweat.

'OK,' she sighed heavily. 'I guess it must be Zachary. What's he done now?'

'Is that the kid's name?' Luke gave a snort of harsh laughter. 'Well, young Zachary is now learning to sit down—*very* carefully!'

'Oh, Luke—you didn't...?'

'Give him a good spanking? Sure I did. And after he'd let down all the tyres of my hired car—which had just been delivered outside the hotel—he's lucky that's all I did to him!'

'But he's only a little boy,' she protested. 'I know he's been naughty, but, well...what he's done isn't so very terrible, is it? In fact,' she grinned, 'I bet that's just the sort of thing you did when you were young—and your kids will probably do exactly the same.'

'I certainly did not, and I'll make sure any children of mine are decently brought up,' he assured her grimly. 'And you can wipe that grin off your face,' he added.

'Because up at the plantation house, you'll find that, not content with harassing *me*, that imp of Satan has also flooded the men's toilet, by stuffing paper into every sink and then turning on the faucets.'

'Oh, no!' she groaned.

Luke's blue eyes glinted with amusement at the sight of her horrified expression. 'Oh, yes! However, there's no need to panic,' he added, catching hold of her arm as she began hurrying past him towards the exit of the small, enclosed garden. 'The hotel staff have now stemmed the flood, and I've also had a few strong, well-chosen words with the kid's father. I don't reckon you'll be having any more trouble from young Zachary.'

'I wish I could believe that,' she muttered, trying to concentrate upon the problem up at the plantation house, but finding herself mindlessly distracted by the warmth of his fingers as he began gently stroking her bare shoulder.

'Maybe...maybe things might have turned out differently for us if we'd had a child...?' he murmured, sliding his other hand about her slim waist.

'A—a child...?' She blinked at him in confusion.

Luke nodded. 'Sure—why not? I'd like to have a boy—a son to follow me,' he said softly, drawing her closer to his tall figure.

She could feel his breath on her cheek, the hard, firm, muscular strength of his body, and the pounding of his heartbeat through his thin cotton shirt. Struggling to control her bemused senses, she inhaled the musky, masculine scent of his cologne, shivering beneath the soft seduction of his hands, now moving slowly and sensuously over her body. For one brief, crazy moment Samantha closed her eyes, forgetting reason and logic as she surrendered to an insidious, rising tide of excitement flowing like quicksilver through her veins; the aching need to surrender to the hard, male body pressed so firmly to her soft breasts and thighs.

'L-Luke!' she gasped desperately.

'Mmm...?' he muttered absently, lowering his dark head to press his lips to the wildly beating pulse at the base of her throat, before trailing his mouth down towards the burgeoning fullness of her breasts. As she lay helpless in his arms, the scorching touch of his hot lips on her bare flesh sent an electric shock zigzagging through her body, and gave her the necessary strength and resolution to quickly wriggle free of his embrace.

'You...you can cut that out!' she croaked, breathing heavily as she tried to control the involuntary trembling in her legs. 'I—I don't know what you think you're playing at, and...and what's with this sudden wish for a child, anyway?'

'It's a perfectly normal desire, surely?'

'If you want a son to follow you—don't look at me, buster!' she retorted quickly. 'One obsessive business-man in the family was one too many, as I found out to my cost!' Her voice was scathing. 'I can assure you that the last thing I want is a child. What I want is a divorce!'

'No.'

'What do you mean, "no"?' she hissed through clenched teeth.

Luke's face was hard as granite. 'I mean exactly what I said: no—I will not give you a divorce.'

'Why ever not?' she demanded with rising fury.

'A better question might be: why should I?' He gave her a slow, cynical smile. 'Hasn't it occurred to you that I might prefer to remain as I am? After all, I have no desire to get married again, and...'

'I'll just bet you haven't!' she fumed angrily. 'You wouldn't like anything to upset your smooth life-style, would you? This way, you can have all the fun you want—with cool blondes like Adele Francis, or dear Corrine—and no responsibility, you...you rat!'

'Don't be so stupid!' he grated. 'Our marriage...'

'Our marriage? Hah! That's a laugh,' she shouted furiously. 'I wasn't married to *you*—I found myself shackled to Brandon Phillips International. And if that isn't unholy wedlock, I don't know what is!'

'That's absolute nonsense! I...'

'*Coo-ee*... Are you there, Luke? I've sketched out a few ideas, and...'

'Oh, great! That's all I need,' Samantha groaned, turning to scowl at Corrine as she walked confidently around the tall hedge of the garden, carrying a large drawing-pad in her hands.

The American girl, looking cool and *soignée*, halted abruptly, and then took a hesitant step backwards, her grey eyes widening as she looked at the two rigidly angry figures who were both now staring at her with equal ferocity. Clearly, the sooner she could extricate herself from what appeared to be an unfortunate scene of some kind, the better.

'This garden is—er—very unusual,' Corrine murmured, turning to look about her. 'However,' she paused, 'I can see that you're—er—busy at the moment, Luke. So if Miss Ward will excuse me...'

Samantha gave an angry snort. 'Hasn't Luke told you the basic facts of life? It's not "Miss Ward"—I only wish it were! Unfortunately, I'm Mrs Luke Brandon—in perpetuity, according to this loathsome husband of mine!' she raged, pointing a shaking finger at Luke. 'However, he tells me that he wants a child, and since I'm *definitely* not available, maybe you'd like to volunteer for the job?' she added with a shrill, hysterical laugh, before taking to her heels and running swiftly back across the lawns to the plantation house.

Upon entering the hotel, Samantha found all her problems fading into insignifince as she discovered that, once again, Thomas was incapable of doing any cooking.

'OK—that's it! You're fired,' she told him as the chef sat slumped over the kitchen table, owlishly regarding her through bleary, drunken eyes. 'If you can't stay sober, then there's no room for you in this hotel.'

'Your aunt...sh-she won't like it,' he hiccuped.

'My aunt's in hospital, and I'm now running this hotel,' Samantha retorted angrily. 'I'll make up your money to the end of the week, and then Lester will take you home, right away.' She turned to the barman who was standing at the top of the kitchen stairs. 'If you'll get the truck out, I'll go along to the office and see to his wages. OK?'

'Sure thing, Miss Ward,' Lester said, coming down and grasping hold of the chef's arm.

'But what are we going to do?' Penny asked anxiously as she followed Samantha into the office.

'I don't know,' Samantha muttered wearily, sitting down at the desk and burying her face in her hands for a moment. 'What about your brother, Marvin? He's a terrific cook. Didn't you say the other day that he was fed up with the management of the Crow's Nest Hotel, and wanted a change of scene?'

Penny hesitated. 'Well...'

'Look, why don't you take an hour off, and go and see your brother?' Samantha pushed a tired hand through her hair. 'I know it's rotten to try and pinch staff from other hotels, but quite frankly, Penny—I'm desperate! If Marvin could join us, it would be an absolute godsend.'

'OK, I'll have a word with him,' the other girl said as Samantha began making up Thomas's wage packet.

'Although I'm certain that even if he agrees to come, there's no way he could leave the Crow's Nest until tomorrow, at the earliest.'

'I've already resigned myself to the fact that our poor, unfortunate guests will have to put up with the dubious pleasure of my cuisine.' Samantha gave her a wry, ironic grin. 'Let's hope and pray that it's only going to be for one day,' she added, handing an envelope to the other girl. 'You can give his wages to our late but unlamented chef. And while you're gone, I'll try and put together some ideas for lunch and dinner.'

Over an hour later, Samantha was still trying to work out a well-balanced menu for dinner that night. She had already wasted far too much time, mostly spent in cursing her own stupidity at so easily surrendering—however briefly—to Luke's overwhelming, sensual magnetism. Despite the fact that he obviously did still find her attractive, he had completely ignored her existence for the past four years, so she certainly wasn't about to begin thinking of herself as a *femme fatale*! Why didn't he leave her alone? Especially when he must have his hands full with Corrine? As for his crazy suggestion that he wanted a child... well, she didn't believe that, not for one moment. Her husband was only interested in one thing—the business of making money. He must have been trying to wind her up... and unfortunately he had succeeded only too well!

'Come on. Forget Luke—you've got to get this menu sorted out,' she muttered to herself as she leafed through a thick book of recipes. At least the problem of lunch had been solved by a quick decision to have a barbecue down at the beach bar; but the evening meal was one to which the guests looked forward, and there was a real problem with adequate supplies of food. Since St Pauls was an island, and everything other than fruit and vegetables had to be imported, it was beginning to look as if she was going to have to rely on what she had in the freezer—something she knew her aunt didn't like to do except in dire emergencies. She was just telling herself that the events of today definitely came under the heading of an emergency, when she suddenly remembered that Lester, the barman, had a cousin who was a fisherman. If she could lay her hands on some lobsters, there were lots of dishes she could prepare, she thought, jotting down some ideas on a pad of paper in front of her. How about having a cream of pumpkin soup to start the meal, with maybe lime syllabub and coconut pie for dessert...?

A knock at the door disturbed her concentration, and her heart leapt into her mouth as she looked up to see Luke entering the room.

'Ah, Samantha...'

'Now what is it?' she demanded aggressively. 'I warn you that I'm definitely not in the mood for any more arguments.'

'Frankly, neither am I,' he said quietly.

'Oh...er...well, that's a relief!' She gave a shaky laugh, grateful for the protection of the large desk which hid her trembling hands from his view.

Luke didn't appear to be in any hurry to break the silence that ensued, his broad-shouldered figure moving to lean casually up against the wall as he surveyed her from beneath his heavy eyelids.

'There are a number of things we have to straighten out between us,' he said at last. 'No—not right now,' he added as she opened her mouth to protest. 'I know you're busy at the moment. But I'm sure you'll agree that we do need to talk—as calmly as possible!—about various matters.'

'All I want to talk about is a divorce!' she snapped nervously.

'I'm prepared to hear what you have to say,' he said quietly.

Her eyes widened. 'Does that mean you've changed your mind?'

Luke shrugged. 'We can discuss it all later. And there's the matter of Corrine...'

'Yes, I—I'm sorry about that,' she said quickly. 'The fact is... well, I've got quite a lot of problems at the moment, and... and while I don't take back anything I said to you, personally—not one word!—I must admit that I was... I was quite unnecessarily rude to Corrine.'

Luke raised a dark eyebrow. 'My dear Samantha—are you sure that you're feeling quite well?' he murmured sardonically.

'OK, OK! You can cut out the wisecracks,' she retorted huskily, aware of her face reddening beneath the mocking gaze from his lazy blue eyes. 'I've said I'm sorry, and if your girlfriend hasn't already begun packing her bags, I'm quite willing to offer her an apology.'

'Good lord!'

'Oh—shut up!' she snapped, before taking a deep breath and trying to hang on to her temper. 'Now, is there anything else you want? Because, I really am busy and...'

'I need to make a phone call.'

'To New York?'

'Yes.'

Samantha shrugged. 'Forget it,' she said dismissively as she began checking through the index of the large, thick cookery book for a recipe for lime syllabub.

'I certainly will not "forget it"!' Luke said curtly, his lips tight with annoyance. 'This hotel, for some strange reason, doesn't appear to have any phones in the guest cottages, so will you please get me that number? At once!' he added, slapping a piece of paper down on the desk in front of her.

'There's no point,' she retorted. 'The phone lines here are chronically bad at this time of day. Just getting through to Antigua could take me hours, and I can't afford to waste the time at the moment. However, if you want to try calling between five and seven o'clock this evening, you might get lucky.'

'I've never heard such nonsense!' he rasped grimly.

'Nonsense or not—it's a fact,' she snapped, putting out a hand to flick the piece of paper back across the desk towards him. 'We do have a radio link with CAT airlines on Antigua for news of incoming passengers— and for serious emergency messages, of course,' she gestured to a handset on the wall behind her, 'but that's it.'

'What a totally ridiculous situation!'

She shrugged. 'Like most islands in this part of the Caribbean, we have to make do with the local telephone service. And it's understandable if the various island governments prefer to spend their money on housing and creating new jobs, rather than laying new phone cables. Why should they pander to the whims of bloated foreign capitalists—such as a certain rich, New York businessman of my acquaintance?' she added nastily.

'*Thank you!*' he ground out through clenched teeth, his cheeks flushed with anger.

'Not at all,' Samantha murmured, giving him a saccharine-sweet smile and suddenly realising, as a fast tide of adrenalin swept through her body, that she felt a whole lot better. Not only had she solved the problem of what to give the hotel guests for dinner tonight, but here was Luke, breathing hell, fire and brimstone—and not being able to do a damn thing about it. In fact, she didn't just feel better, she felt really great!

'Have you any other queries?' she asked. 'I am very busy, you know.'

'Yes, so I believe,' Luke drawled, his lips curving into a grim smile. 'I hear, via the hotel grapevine, that you've just sacked your chef.'

'What nonsense,' she snapped, her heart sinking as she raised her chin and stared him straight in the eye. OK, so she was lying, but she must try and scotch this rumour as quickly as possible. Staffing problems could empty a hotel every bit as fast as a rampant, infectious disease. 'I think that you'll find our chef will be producing the usual excellent meal tonight.'

'Hmm...' He looked at her from beneath his heavy eyelids for a moment, before his lips began to twitch with wry amusement. 'You've certainly changed during the past four years, Samantha,' he grinned mockingly. 'But I'm pleased to see that you're still a very bad liar.'

Their eyes duelled, and she could feel her cheeks flushing as her heart began beating a rapid tattoo in her chest. 'Oh...go away!' she mumbled.

'I particularly like the reference to "our chef".' Luke gave a cruel laugh. 'I can hardly wait to discover if my wife's cooking has improved since the days when she could hardly boil an egg!'

'Get out of here!' she shouted furiously, grabbing a silver paperweight and throwing it at the tall figure who was shaking with laughter.

To her rage and chagrin he caught the missile in mid-air with infuriating ease. 'Good luck, sweetheart—tonight's meal will undoubtedly be one to remember!' he taunted, before striding towards the door, the sound of his sardonic laughter echoing down the corridor behind him.

Remembering Luke's words, some eight hours later, Samantha brushed the damp hair from her brow and tried to concentrate on whipping up egg whites for the meringue topping to the coconut dessert.

She'd show him! This dinner tonight was going to be a *fantastic* success, and then Luke would be sorry, she promised herself, knowing that her reaction was childish, but unable to banish the fury and resentment which still flowed through her veins. He should try running a hotel, she thought grimly. In fact, she'd swap jobs with him any day! Being in control of a large public company simply had to be kids' play, compared to all the traumas of her present occupation. She'd nearly gone mad attempting to expand recipes for six or eight into the correct quantities for all their guests. As far as she could see, hotel chefs required a Masters degree in mathematics before they even set foot in a kitchen!

Wiping the sweat from her brow, and trying to ignore the uncomfortable fact that her evening dress was sticking to her damp, perspiring body, Samantha quickly spooned the meringue on to the cooked coconut mixture, and put the heavy tray of dishes into a cool oven. Fervently praying that tonight of all nights the generator wouldn't break down, she glanced across the kitchen to where Betty Finberg, ignoring the nervous tension in the kitchen, was calmly teaching two of the young kitchen girls how to finely chop up an onion. What a marvellous friend and help the elderly American woman had been!

Organising a barbecue lunch down at the beach bar had been relatively easy, and Lester's cousin had been able to provide all the lobsters she needed. But Samantha had become increasingly panic-stricken when she realised just what was involved in cooking a complicated three-course menu for all the hotel guests. Desperately appealed to for help, Betty had willingly volunteered her services, and had also come up with a marvellous recipe for Lobster Creole, served on a bed of rice.

It had been a terrific scramble to get half the food prepared, and then dash off to the sugar mill to quickly change into a long evening dress, before returning to the damp, muggy kitchen to continue the final preparation of the meal. But everything seemed to be coming along smoothly, Samantha thought, quickly tasting the pumpkin soup simmering on the stove beside her, before glancing up at the large clock on the wall. Six-thirty— only an hour to go! Surely they'd never be ready on time? And she nearly yelped with dismay as she realised that she hadn't yet begun making the lime syllabub.

Dashing about the room like one demented, she gathered up the necessary ingredients and had just finished whipping the cream when she was distracted by the ringing of the telephone attached to the wall beside the stoves.

'Yes ... yes, who is it?' she said breathlessly, tipping sherry into the cream with one hand, while holding the receiver with another. 'Oh, Gerald...' she wailed. 'I really can't talk now. I'm frantically busy.'

'I just wanted to say that I'm sailing the yacht over to St Pauls tomorrow, and maybe you'd like to come for a sail in the afternoon?'

'Well, I don't know...' she muttered, tucking the phone under her chin as she added lime juice to the mixture in the large bowl.

'I know that with your aunt away, you're run off your feet; but surely you'll be free after the guests have had their lunch?' he pressed.

'Yes, I should think... Hold on a moment,' she added, her eyes widening in startled surprise as she saw Luke striding across the kitchen towards her. 'What on earth are you doing here—slumming?' she demanded, her gaze sweeping over his tall figure clothed in an elegant, white evening-jacket.

Luke halted in front of her, his mouth tight with fury. 'I have been trying, for the last hour and a half, to make an extremely important call to New York,' he thundered. 'I don't mind waiting while other guests are on the phone, but I'm damned if I'm going to stand patiently by while you and your boyfriend arrange a cosy date together!'

'How dare you listen in to my private conversation?' Samantha gasped, her voice high and shrill with rage.

'With the utmost reluctance, I can assure you!' he grated. 'Now—get off that phone. Right this minute!'

'I certainly will not!' she retorted fiercely. 'I shall talk as long as I like, and... *what do you think you're doing?*' she cried as he seized the receiver from her hand.

'Good evening—er—Gerald. I don't think we've met,' he murmured, easily fending off Samantha's attempts to grab hold of the phone.

'Who's that? And what in the hell's going on...?' Gerald demanded, clearly confused by the strange male voice and the shrieks of rage in the background as Samantha, after a long and trying day, finally lost all control.

'There's nothing to worry about, Gerald. It's only my wife... demonstrating that she has a temper to match the colour of her hair!' Luke's sardonic laugh was cut short by a grunt of pain as Samantha brought her stiletto heel firmly down on to his foot.

'What do you mean, *"your wife"*?' Gerald shouted down the line, but he failed to obtain an answer, hearing only the confusing sounds of a mêlée in the background, before the call was abruptly terminated and he was left with only the dialling tone in his ear.

Arms and legs flailing wildly, it wasn't until Betty's shocked face swam into view that Samantha began to try and pull herself together. Unfortunately, she had left it just a little too late. Sobering up fast from the all-consuming rage which had possessed her a few seconds before, she glanced down with dismay at the smashed crockery littering the kitchen floor, and then turned to look at her husband.

'*Oh, my God...!*' she breathed, her green eyes widening with horror as she gazed at the sight of his tall, elegantly dressed figure completely drenched—head to foot—in lime syllabub. Had she really picked up the bowl and thrown the contents all over him? 'You . . . you look like a s-snowman!' she gasped, unable to prevent herself from giving way to a peal of hysterical laughter at Luke's expression of outraged incredulity, as he grabbed a cloth and began to vigorously wipe the cream from his face and hair.

'I'll teach you to laugh at me—you redheaded devil!' he bellowed.

As she ruefully conceded to herself later, Samantha was late off the mark. By the time she divined her husband's intentions, and began backing nervously away, it was far too late. Moving swiftly forward, Luke grabbed hold of her arm and swung her hard up against his body, thereby quickly and efficiently transferring at least half of the syllabub mixture on to her own dress, which was inadequately protected by a small apron tied around her waist.

'What's wrong, sweetheart? Lost your sense of humour, have you?' he grated as she shrieked at the disgusting sensation of cold, clammy dessert trickling down inside the low-cut neckline of her dress.

'Let me go,' she begged hoarsely. Twisting and struggling to escape from the hard arms tightening like bands of steel about her slim figure, there was nothing she could do as he lowered his dark head, his mouth possessing her lips with scorching heat and passion.

'I don't want to be a killjoy—but I hope you two young people realise that it's almost time to serve dinner?'

Betty's dry voice broke through the mists in Samantha's brain, and must have simultaneously affected Luke as she felt his arms grow slack, and heard the rasping sound as he cursed violently beneath his breath.

Opening her dazed eyes, she focused on Luke's tanned, strained features, still covered with streaks of cream, and then looked down at her dress with mounting consternation. 'Oh, no! Look what you've done!' she cried.

'Just a small *quid pro quo*, sweetheart,' he drawled, his eyes gleaming with amusement as she began moaning helplessly to herself, desperately waving her hands in the air as she tried to think what to do.

'I suggest that, like myself, you'd better go and have a shower before changing your clothes,' he remarked blandly, putting out a hand to wipe some cream off her nose. 'Umm—delicious,' he grinned as he licked his finger. 'Almost—but not quite—as sweet and delicious as your lips!'

As exit lines went, it was a sure-fire winner! Samantha's stormy eyes followed the tall figure of her husband as he strode out of the kitchen, before she sank down on to a chair and buried her face in her hands.

'We'll clear up the mess, dear, and I've just told Penny to tell the guests they're welcome to a free drink on the house, since the meal will be just a little late,' Betty said quietly some minutes later, avoiding Samantha's eyes as she directed the girls to clean up the kitchen. 'Why not go and have a nice warm bath and get changed?' she added. 'There's actually plenty of time before dinner is served.'

Samantha sighed and rose wearily to her feet. 'Yes. I—I won't be too long,' she muttered, taking a deep breath and forcing herself to walk slowly out of the kitchen. Making her way through the back of the hotel, she held her head stiffly in the air and ignored the startled murmurs of the staff; acting as if it was a perfectly normal, everyday occurrence that her long evening dress should be covered, from shoulder to hem, with the cold, congealing remains of what had once been lime syllabub.

CHAPTER FIVE

DIVING off the raft moored out in the middle of the bay, Samantha almost groaned with pleasure as she savoured the cool sea water on her heated skin. Swimming strongly and rhythmically towards one of the stone breakwaters which edged the small bay, she pulled herself up on to the warm, smooth concrete surface and sat down on the towel which she had left there earlier.

Lord—it was hot! The blistering heat was very unusual for this time of year, as was the steamy, sweltering level of humidity. The air was so close and still, without even a breath of air to cool one's skin—or one's temper, for that matter.

She gave a heavy sigh, grimacing as she tried in vain to banish the horrendous events of yesterday from her mind; the dismal fact that she had—once again—lost her temper and made an absolutely first-class fool of herself. Why couldn't she just ignore Luke? It was stupid to allow herself to be provoked so easily; and why on earth did she seem to be consumed by such a burning desire to wound and hurt him as much as possible, which only resulted in her feeling more confused and unhappy herself?

Wishing she could draw a permanent veil over last night's embarrassing incident, Samantha still didn't know where she'd found the strength to return to the kitchen. Shampooing the disgusting, gooey mess from her hair, getting dressed in a fresh dress and having to walk back down the steps into that hot, steamy inferno had taken every ounce of resolution that she possessed. But

85

nothing—absolutely nothing—could have persuaded her to go up to the dining-room at the end of the meal.

'I can't do it, Betty,' she had wailed, her legs seeming to turn to water at the thought of having to face Luke once again.

'Relax. Calm down, honey,' Betty had said, taking her arm and steering her trembling figure towards a chair. 'It's obviously been a traumatic evening—so I'm going to pour us both a stiff brandy. I reckon we've earned it!'

'You certainly have,' Samantha agreed fervently. 'The dinner was really terrific. I simply don't know what I'd have done without your help.' She stared miserably down at the golden liquid in the glass which Betty placed in front of her. 'I'm really very sorry about . . . well, about everything that happened tonight. I don't know what came over me . . .' she sighed helplessly. 'If only Luke would get the hell out of my life!'

'That strikingly handsome man . . .? Is he really your husband?'

Samantha nodded glumly. 'We've been separated for four years, during which time he has completely ignored my existence. And now he's suddenly reappeared on the scene. Not only is he busy playing the heavy husband, but he's also refusing to give me a divorce. I wish I knew what he's up to.'

'Maybe he's still in love with you?'

'*What* . . .?'

'Why not?' Betty smiled at the startled expression on Samantha's face. 'After all, you're a very beautiful girl, and he . . .' She hesitated, searching for the right words. 'Well, he did seem to be in quite an emotional, over-wrought state.'

Samantha gave a short bark of grim, bitter laughter. 'Emotional? The man's a calculating machine, with nothing but ice in his veins! Running away from him was the best decision I've ever made.'

'Well, Hector and I reckon that it's a real shame for you to be living on this island, with just an old woman for company. I know you and Emily really care for each other,' Betty added quickly. 'But your aunt's done what she wanted to with her life—and enjoyed every minute, by all accounts. Don't you think it's time you stopped hiding here, on St Pauls, and spread your wings a little? Life in the big outside world isn't so terrible, you know.'

The younger girl stared at her with astonishment. 'Oh, come on, Betty. I've got all my gift shops on the islands, and a host of friends both here and in Antigua. Of course I'm not "hiding" from anyone or anything. What an extraordinary idea!'

'Is it? I reckon that you ought to have a good, hard think about that. And now, I also reckon it's time for you and me to hit the sack,' Betty said briskly. 'I'm all in, and you look exhausted. Believe me, honey, you'll feel much better after a good night's sleep.'

But she hadn't slept well. Not that Betty's extraordinary suggestion had disturbed her. Her life was full to overflowing at the moment and, in fact, a little peace and quiet would be very welcome. No, it was her husband who'd been the problem. Tossing and turning throughout the long night and early hours of the morning, there had been nothing she could do to banish the flickering images of Luke's hard, formidable presence as he stalked relentlessly through her dreams. Waking early, and feeling every bit as much of a wrung-out dishrag as she had the previous morning, Samantha had been cheered by Penny's news that not only was her brother, Marvin, prepared to act as chef at the hotel, but that he was willing to begin work straight away.

Unfortunately, that piece of good news was quickly followed by an abusive phone call from the owner of the Crow's Nest Hotel. She had tried to apologise, explaining just how desperate she had been. But her excuse hadn't seemed to cut much ice with Marvin's ex-employer, who now found himself in the same awkward position as she had experienced yesterday: '...and I don't even know how to open a can of beans!' he had raged, before slamming down the phone.

The rest of the morning hadn't been much better. There had been a cry for help from a manageress of one of her shops, passed on via the radio link with CAT, but there didn't seem to be anything she could do about it, since the phone lines had been out of action again. Not only had she spent ages trying to get a call through to her aunt, with absolutely no success, but she was also beginning to wonder if she had a case of galloping persecution-mania as she tried to keep well out of Luke and Corrine's way. Something that had proved to be extremely difficult to achieve.

Goodness knew what the couple were up to, but they had spent most of the morning walking around and through the hotel. Looking up at the outside of the building, examining the silk walls of the dining-room, and even venturing down into the bowels of the damp, dark kitchen—Luke and Corrine were everywhere! So, when she received a message from the housekeeper, she had sighed helplessly and given up the unequal struggle against malign fate.

'I'm told that you want to borrow a hairdryer,' Samantha said, as Corrine answered her tentative knock on the door of the American girl's bungalow. 'And I'd like to take this opportunity to...well, apologise for my behaviour yesterday,' she added, handing the dryer to the girl as she followed her into the large sitting-room.

'That's OK.' Corrine shrugged. 'I realised that your quarrel was with Mr Brandon and not with me.'

Samantha blinked, thrown completely off course by the girl's calm, dispassionate view of what must have been an embarrassing experience. 'Yes, well...I was very rude, and I wanted you to know just how sorry I am...'

Her voice trailed nervously away as Corrine continued to regard her with a composed, serene expression on her face. Didn't anything disturb this girl? she thought wildly. Even her clothes seemed to reflect her personality. Samantha had never seen her wearing anything other than tones of cream and beige, and again today Corrine was looking cool, elegant and extremely beautiful in an ivory-coloured sundress. Suddenly feeling overwhelmingly depressed in the presence of such perfection, she was just turning to leave when a hotel waiter arrived with a tray, and Corrine asked her to stay and have a cup of coffee.

'Well...' She hesitated. Maybe she ought to try and repair some of the damage she'd caused yesterday? 'Yes, OK, just a small one.'

'The island seems to be charming, and this is a wonderful position for a hotel,' Corrine said, handing her a cup. 'Mr Brandon tells me that you've lived here for some years.'

'Yes, that's right.'

'And you run it with your aunt, I believe?'

'Yes.'

'I was sorry to hear that your aunt is in hospital in Antigua, although Mr Brandon says that she's recovering well from her hip operation.'

Well, well—that really *is* interesting! Samantha thought, striving to maintain a bland expression on her face as her brain whirled into top gear. She could kick herself for not having noticed the fact before now: but ever since his arrival on the island, *Luke had never once mentioned Aunt Emily*. It wasn't surprising that she, herself, hadn't brought up the subject—the shock of his sudden appearance, and their violent confrontations had banished everything else from her mind. But since she hadn't mentioned her aunt's accident and hospitalis-ation, how did Luke and his girlfriend know all about it...? There was something very odd going on here—and what was all this 'Mr Brandon' business?

Trying not to make her scrutiny too obvious, she gazed about the room. There didn't seem to be any evidence of Luke's presence, but then, he wouldn't be interested in spending too much time in the sitting-room of the bungalow, would he? she thought grimly, casting a sour glance at the door which led to the large bedroom.

'Have you known my ex-husband for long?' she asked casually.

'Well, I've known *of* him for some time, of course,' Corrine replied. 'But I've only been working for him for the last two months.'

'Ah, I did wonder...I mean, you do refer to him rather formally, if I may say so.'

Corrine gave her a thin smile. 'It might, perhaps, save some time and speculation on your part, if I tell you that Mr Brandon and I have a purely business relationship.'

'Oh, yes?' Samantha murmured, her voice heavy with scepticism.

'I can assure you that I'm speaking the truth,' the other girl said coldly. 'Although...' She hesitated, a faint flush staining her cheeks. 'If you and your husband are about to have a divorce...' She gave a cool shrug of her shoulders. 'That does seem to leave the field wide open, doesn't it?'

'Does it?' Samantha gave a grim laugh. 'Oh, boy—are you in for a surprise! Surely you must have come across Adele Francis?'

Corrine looked at her with a puzzled frown. 'Adele Francis? Who's she?'

'One of his personal assistants. A very beautiful girl, who looks remarkably like you, in fact.'

The American girl shook her head. 'No... no, I don't think I know anyone of that name.'

'Well, if you fancy your chances with my ex-husband—and especially if you've got the sound of wedding bells ringing in your ears—then not only are you out of your mind, but I guess you'd better get yourself a pair of hobnail boots,' Samantha grated, banging her cup down on a nearby table. 'Because, if you are looking forward to connubial bliss with Luke, the first thing you'll have to do is to kick Adele Francis out of the marital bed!' she added harshly as she turned to go, her trembling figure bumping against a large portfolio, and dislodging the contents which spilled all over the floor.

'Oh, lord, I'm s-sorry,' she said, quickly bending down to gather up the drawings. 'I—I didn't realise you were an artist,' she added, looking down at a picture of the front of the hotel.

'I'm not. Strictly speaking, I'm an architect. These are just a few rough sketches—some ideas I had.'

'They're... they really are very good,' Samantha mused slowly, still kneeling as she examined the pictures more closely. 'I see you've widened the hotel entrance. It—well, it certainly makes the place look much more impressive.'

'And far more practical, as well,' Corrine said, sounding animated for the first time as she bent down to point out various aspects of the drawings. '... and I also thought that there was a need for wheelchair access at the side of the building, as well as making it easier to move baggage trolleys in and out of the hotel.'

'That's a brilliant idea,' Samantha murmured, before rising slowly to her feet. 'Look, I . . . well, I'm sorry if I've been sounding off like a first-class bitch. Luke and I . . .' She paused, swallowing against a sudden, hard lump in her throat as she turned to leave. 'I guess what I'm trying to say—rather badly—is that Luke and I were all washed up long before you came on the scene. There's no way you're to blame for what went wrong with our marriage.' She gave a helpless shrug. 'It was all pretty hopeless, anyway . . .'

'You're still in love with him, aren't you?' Corrine said quietly.

'You have to be kidding!' Samantha gave a harsh bark of laughter, a hectic flush spreading over her cheeks as she moved towards the door. 'How could I possibly be in love with a man like Luke? Someone who regards a wife as far less important than his business activities, *or* his partiality for cool blondes? Oh, boy—I'd really need to have my head examined, wouldn't I?'

And you never spoke a truer word! Samantha told herself grimly, slipping off the breakwater and down into the sea for a last, cool dip before going back to the hotel. That strange girl, Corrine, didn't know what she was getting into, but if she wanted Luke, she must be nuts. And as for . . . Her thoughts were rudely interrupted as she felt a hand grab hold of her right foot, tugging her down beneath the water. She kicked out, frantically trying to free herself as she bobbed up to the surface.

'Ouch—that hurt.'

'Serve you right!' she spluttered, trying to catch her breath, her heart still thumping with fright as she stared at Luke's sleek, wet head surfacing beside her. 'What are you doing here, anyway?'

'Bathing in the sea, of course—what else?' he mocked, a disturbing gleam in his blue eyes as he gazed at her breasts, inadequately covered by either her skimpy white bikini, or the still, crystal-clear water.

Samantha glared at him. 'You know that isn't what I meant,' she retorted, twisting away to avoid his hands as he tried to clasp hold of her waist. Swimming quickly over to the breakwater, she climbed up to sit down on the concrete wall.

'Hey—that's mine,' she said indignantly as she turned to see Luke had swiftly followed her example, and was now using her towel to dry his face.

He gave a bark of sardonic laughter. 'Wow—it sounds as if you got out of the wrong side of the bed this morning!'

'Unlike you—at least I got out of my *own* bed this morning!' she flashed back, before clasping her arms about her legs and burying her burning face against her knees. Why did she always go immediately on to the attack with Luke? Why couldn't she have held her tongue—just for once? Feeling sick with apprehension, she waited for the storm to break about her head.

To her surprise, Luke didn't say anything for a while, and then she heard him give a sigh and felt the touch of his hand on her back. 'Let's cool it, huh?' he murmured.

The warmth of his fingers as they stroked her skin had a calming, almost soporific effect on her ragged emotions, and she slowly turned her head to gaze at the man sitting beside her. And that was a mistake, she re-alised as she found herself unable to tear her eyes away from his broad shoulders, the tanned skin and dark, hairy chest still covered with glistening drops of water. A sudden spasm of excitement deep in her stomach broke through her bemused state, and, heeding the urgent warning of her body, she quickly sat up.

'I'm sorry to snap like that,' she mumbled, grabbing the towel and concentrating on drying her hair. Honestly—she'd done nothing for the last two days but apologise right, left and centre. She was fed up to the back teeth with always finding herself in the wrong, and... Oh, lord—any minute now Luke was going to mention the scene in the kitchen last night, and if she didn't say she was sorry—*yet again*—they'd be straight into an argument. Her heart sank at the prospect of yet another furious quarrel with her husband.

'About last night...' He paused.

She shuddered. 'Please, Luke, I—I can't bear to even think about it.'

'You're not the only one! How about if we both write the episode down to a mutual loss of temper, and agree to forget it, hmm? In fact,' he added with a slight laugh, 'I would definitely appreciate some sort of non-aggression treaty—for a few days, at least!'

'So would I,' she agreed shyly, glancing up at him through her eyelashes, her cheeks flushing as she met his warm, lazy smile.

Neither of them said any more for some time, Samantha surprised to find that for the first time since his arrival, she was able to relax in Luke's company.

'My mother would love it here,' he said, his voice breaking into the companionable silence. 'This must be one of the most peaceful places I've ever come across.'

'How is your mother?'

'She's fine, although nowadays she prefers to spend the winter in a warmer climate than New York.'

'And Barbara?' Samantha asked. Other than a few brief letters and an occasional card at Christmas, there had been no real contact between them for the past four years. 'The last time I heard from her, she was working for some whizz-kid on Madison Avenue.'

He laughed. 'And driving him up the wall, I expect! I don't need to tell you that my kid sister was always far keener on her busy social life than on being a career girl. And when she met a Frenchman, Edmond Vignaux, she quickly threw up her job to get married. In fact, she's on her honeymoon, right now.'

'That's great news.' Samantha smiled at him. 'I do hope she'll be very happy. And now, I really must go,' she added, quickly rising to her feet. 'You'll undoubtedly be pleased to hear that we have a new chef starting today, so I must go and see that all's well in the kitchen.'

'Just a minute,' he said, catching hold of her hand as she bent down to pick up her towel. 'We've still got a lot of things to thrash out between us.'

'I'm far too busy,' she muttered, trying to tug her hand away from his firm grasp. 'Don't be silly—let me go,' she pleaded as he, too, stood up while still maintaining his grip on her wrist.

'I want to have a long, serious talk to you,' he said firmly. 'So, when's it to be?'

'Oh, for heaven's sakes—I don't know.'

'This afternoon?'

'Yes . . . OK . . . all right!' she said quickly as he began pulling her closer to his tall figure. 'You're nothing but a bully!' she ground out, massaging her wrist as he let go of her hand.

He gave her a mocking grin. 'I'm not going to quarrel with you, Samantha. Not when I now know *just* how to get you to do what I want.' He laughed as her cheeks flushed a deep crimson before she turned on her heel and began walking quickly away.

'Now, don't forget. We have a date for this afternoon,' he called out after her swiftly moving figure.

Oh, no! Her mind and body seemed to be in a chaotic state of contradictory and disorientating emotions, but as she made her way back to the hotel she knew with absolute certainty that she must find some way of avoiding Luke's disturbing presence. He seemed to have guessed that she was anxious not to have any close, intimate contact with him. And of course he was quite right—she wasn't a total idiot! It was all very well for Luke to say that he wanted to talk, but the only talking he had done so far had rapidly ended up with her being clasped firmly in his arms. And wasn't that just like a man? They seemed to think that sex was the answer to everything. Well it *certainly* wasn't, she told herself roughly, desperately trying to ignore the confusing, sick, fluttering feeling in the pit of her stomach. The answer—if not to everything, to at least most of her problems—was to find some way of avoiding her husband. It wasn't because she was intent on running away again, she reassured herself, recalling Betty's words last night as she marched into the sugar mill to shower and change. It was because she was feeling so bewildered and confused by her mental and physical reaction to Luke that she simply had to find some time and space in which to try and think calmly about the situation—something she couldn't do here, at the hotel.

As she stood beneath the cascading water, the answer suddenly struck her with a blinding flash. Of course! Now she had Marvin in the kitchen, she could safely leave Penny to run the hotel for a few days. All she had to do was to get into the aeroplane and fly away—what could be simpler than that? It would mean getting up very early tomorrow morning, of course, and taking off for another island, but which one...? A moment or two later she hit on the obvious answer: St Barts.

The four gift shops, which she owned on the islands within easy flying distance of Antigua, were running smoothly and doing very well. It was only the fifth, opened last year on the French island of St Barts, which seemed to be having constant teething troubles. The message she'd received this morning from Janina, the manageress, had raised yet more problems. She had known that she really ought to fly over there and sort matters out as soon as possible, but up to now she hadn't seen how she could manage to do so.

At the sudden prospect of having some time away from the hotel—and the pressure being exerted by Luke—her spirits rose dramatically. In fact, apart from her presence being necessary in the kitchen during lunch and dinner, she could shut herself away, here in the sugar mill, for the rest of the day. And if her husband wanted to have a talk... well, that was just too bad, wasn't it?

It was well over two hours later when Samantha returned to her refuge in the sugar mill, the fresh dress she had put on before lunch already damp and clinging to her figure. Even the guests were beginning to complain about the excessive heat and the almost unbearable humidity. Maybe the storm forecast by Jason would clear the air? she thought hopefully, going straight into the bathroom to have yet another cold shower.

At least she'd managed to get through to Aunt Emily who, as she had rightly guessed, had been hopping mad at not having heard from her niece for two days. Samantha grinned as she recalled some of the old woman's language. If anyone else had been listening on the line, they'd have had a blue fit! she thought, not bothering to dry or cover herself as she left the bathroom in search of some fresh clothing.

'What the hell...?' she gasped, hardly able to believe the evidence of her own eyes as she came to a sudden, startled halt at the top of the open staircase.

'Ah, Samantha, here you are at last,' Luke said, smiling lazily up at her as he lay comfortably stretched out on her bed, his arms folded behind his dark head.

'Do make yourself at home!' she invited with angry sarcasm, scowling down at the bronze limbs of the figure, clothed only in a pair of white shorts, who was lying there as if he owned the place.

'Umm...very nice!' he murmured appreciatively as he gazed up at her naked body.

Oh, no! She'd been so startled and angry that she'd completely forgotten... 'You—you rat!' she wailed, quickly diving towards a chair and grabbing the first garment she could lay hands on. 'Shut your eyes,' she commanded as she scrambled into a thin muslin gown, wrapping it tightly around her wet, trembling figure and swiftly tying the sash. Turning to confront him, she found herself being regarded by a pair of gleaming blue eyes. 'You were looking,' she accused him bleakly.

He gave her a mocking smile. 'How could I be expected to resist such an entrancing sight?' he said, his gaze moving slowly over the beautiful girl who was glaring at him with such fury. This was possibly *not* the time to tell his wife that the sight of the thin gown, clinging so tightly to her damp body and full breasts, whose swollen rosy tips were clearly visible as they thrust against the diaphanous material, presented a far more sexy and provocative sight than her nude body had done.

'Relax, sweetheart,' he murmured. 'This isn't the first time I've seen you without any clothes. We were married and lived together for a year—if you remember?'

'How could I ever forget?' she ground out harshly. 'What do you think you're doing here?'

'You agreed to meet me for a talk, this afternoon.' He yawned and stretched his long body. 'I got tired of waiting for you and decided to take a short nap.'

Samantha glowered. 'Oh, you did, did you? Well, you can take your nap somewhere else! Come on, Luke— playtime's over. I want you to get up, get out, and—if I'm *really* lucky—to get lost!'

'Oh, no. You and I have some important matters to discuss, and I intend staying here until we do so. All night, if necessary,' he added, a deep rumble of laughter shaking his broad-shouldered frame.

It was his vile laughter that did it. Thinking about the episode later, and seeking some rational explanation for her quite deplorable behaviour, it occurred to Samantha that Luke might have deliberately tried to provoke her. If so, he had certainly succeeded! As the sound of his laugh echoed around the room, a thick red mist seemed to cloud her vision, her body shaking and trembling as she was suddenly overcome by an avalanche of overwhelming rage and fury. With an exasperated cry, she scooped up one of his shoes from the floor and rushed blindly towards the bed.

She did, of course, have the advantage of surprise, but there was no doubt that her impromptu weapon proved to be surprisingly effective. Raining blows down upon her husband, Samantha was successfully inflicting some considerable damage before her victim managed to gather his superior forces, and swiftly began taking retaliatory action. The shoe was wrenched from her hand, and a moment later she found herself sprawled on her back with Luke's hard, heavy body pinning her firmly to the mattress as he glared down into her dazed eyes.

'OK—that's *it*, sweetheart!' he snarled, breathing heavily. 'You have some lessons to learn, and lesson number one is: when I tell my wife that I want to talk to her—I expect her to listen to what I have to say! *Do-I-make-myself-clear?*' he demanded savagely through clenched teeth.

'As daylight—you foul bully! Let me go,' she panted, wincing with pain as the fingers grasping her shoulders bit like talons into her soft flesh.

'Oh, no. Not until you and I have the discussion from which you've been running away for the past two days. It won't take long,' he assured her with a grim smile. 'I have other plans for this afternoon.'

'Big deal!' she muttered, trying to wriggle from beneath his heavy body.

'Don't do that . . . or I won't be responsible for my actions!' his voice rasped, but she had already felt the warning, heated pressure of the body stirring against hers, had recognised the message conveyed by the glittering eyes staring so fixedly down into her own.

She froze, hardly daring to breathe. However much she wanted to hit him on his determined chin, it seemed as if her only route out of this *very* fraught situation lay in calm, reasoned argument.

'All right, Luke.' She swallowed nervously. 'I'll listen to what you have to say, but please let go of my arms because you're hurting me.'

'I don't trust you an inch,' he said flatly, but he relaxed his cruel grip, raising a hand to brush away a lock of dark hair which had fallen over his brow, and grimacing as his fingers touched the corner of his eye. 'I reckon you've given me a black eye. Thanks a bunch, sweetheart!' he grated.

'Oh, dear . . .' she murmured, trying not to smile as she noted a dark bruise already forming on his skin.

There was no doubt about it, Luke was going to look really terrible in a few hours' time!

'Don't laugh too soon—you're hardly in a fit state yourself,' he drawled, grinning as she raised her head and realised, with dawning horror, that her gown had become completely undone. 'However, since I want to talk to you, I think we'd better cover these lovely breasts of yours, hmm?'

Samantha clamped her eyelids shut as he adjusted the garment, a deep tide of crimson sweeping over her face at the touch of his fingers, which seemed to be brushing quite unnecessarily often across her swollen nipples. 'That's enough!' she croaked, desperately trying to ignore the flames of desire flicking through her trembling body. 'I—I thought you said you wanted to talk,' she added breathlessly.

'So I do.' His body continuing to hold her pinned firmly beneath him, he stared silently down into her green eyes. 'You've changed so much, Samantha—almost beyond recognition.' He shook his head, his lips curving into a warm, intimate smile. 'I married a beautiful child, and now I find that she's become a vitally attractive, very desirable woman.'

'There's no need to turn on the heavy charm,' she said caustically, painfully aware of her quickening heartbeat, and the way her pulse seemed to be racing out of control. 'Of course I've changed. It's been four years, for heaven's sake! And now you've got the brass nerve to suddenly turn up here out of the blue—just who in the hell do you think you are?'

'Your husband,' he grated harshly.

'Oh, yeah...? Big deal!'

There was a heavy silence for a moment, shivers of apprehension feathering down her spine as she saw a muscle tighten along his jaw, his eyes narrowing to an icy glare. 'Don't push me too far, Samantha,' he thundered. 'Believe me—there's no way I'm prepared to have my wife indulging in a rip-roaring, public love affair with some damned Englishman!'

'I'm not!'

'Oh, yeah?' he echoed, his cynical, mocking drawl bringing a hectic flush to her cheeks.

'You don't understand...'

'You're damn right, I don't,' he growled menacingly.

'...Gerald and I...we don't...well, we don't have that sort of relationship,' she muttered, her face growing scarlet beneath the unwavering scrutiny of his cold blue eyes.

'The man's obviously a fool!' Luke gave a harsh bark of laughter. 'OK, sweetheart, let's get this business sorted out once and for all, hmm? In words of one syllable— have you, or have you not, slept with the guy?'

'*Well...?*' he demanded fiercely as she remained obstinately silent, glaring resentfully up at the hard, implacable expression on his face.

'All right...all right, there's no need to shout,' she said bitterly. 'If you must know—no I haven't. And now, will you kindly mind your own business?'

Luke stared silently down, his eyes boring into hers for what seemed eternity. 'You're still my wife, Samantha,' he said at last. 'And therefore what you do is very much my business.'

She gave an angry laugh. 'On the principal of "What's mine is mine"?'

He shrugged. 'While you remain married to me, I'm not prepared to have anyone messing around with my wife.'

'OK—fine. Agree to a divorce, and then there won't be a problem.'

'There's going to be no divorce,' he said flatly.

'But...but you said...'

'I said that I would listen to what you have to say—that's all.' He pushed a hand roughly through his dark hair. 'Against my better judgement I once listened to your aunt, *and* took her advice. Never again!'

'Aunt Emily?' She gazed at him in astonishment. 'Are you trying to tell me that you—and my aunt—have been interfering in my life behind my back? I—I don't believe she'd ever do such a thing.'

Luke sighed, moving his body to allow her to sit up. 'You were so young when I married you—half-child, half-woman—and still confused by your father's death at the time you ran away. Where else would you go, but to your aunt?' His eyes grew bleak, his mouth tightening into a grim line. 'Of course I talked to her. It was obvious that you were deeply miserable and unhappy with me, and I needed advice on how to cope with the situation.'

'I don't know about coping—but as far as our marriage was concerned, you certainly didn't try very hard, did you?' she retorted. 'You left me alone, day after day, in what you must have known was a totally alien environment.' She brushed aside the tangled length of her curly hair. 'There was nothing for me to do in that huge apartment, but you wouldn't let me have even a part-time job, would you? You were totally obsessed by your business affairs...'

'Did you really expect me to dance attendance on you morning, noon and night?' he rasped.

'No, of course not. But you never discussed any of your business deals with me, for instance, and you made it quite clear that I came a very poor second to your work. A poor third, in fact, if we take Adele Francis into account!' she added bitterly.

'Adele?'

She gave an unhappy laugh. 'You really are the pits, aren't you? You've been getting all steamed up about my relationship with Gerald—but we haven't heard a word about *your* love affair, have we? Talk about double standards!'

'What love affair?' he growled.

'*Hah!* Is your personal assistant still providing her very *personal* assistance? I bet you two have a lot of fun together! Do you remember all those nights you spent in the office?' Samantha asked, her voice husky with painful memories. 'I used to lie alone in bed, imagining you and Adele together. Only I didn't have to use my imagination for very long, because she was only too happy to tell me all about your intimate relationship, wasn't she?'

'And you believed her?' His voice rose angrily.

'Adele told me, time and again, that you and she...'

'Spare me the sordid details!' he said curtly, his eyes glinting dangerously.

Samantha stared at him in confusion. 'Didn't you...? I mean—was Adele lying to me all the time?'

He swore under his breath, rolling on to his back and staring up at the ceiling. 'I don't think that whether Adele was telling the truth or not is of any relevance at the moment,' he said grimly. 'You were quite ready to believe that I'd have an affair with a member of my staff, and you apparently couldn't even trust me so far as to talk about your suspicions.'

'But I did! I told you that if you insisted on taking Adele off to Rio...'

'For God's sake!' he exploded. 'That was hardly a discussion—just the usual half-baked complaint that you had in those days! How on earth was I supposed to alter all my arrangements, just because you'd taken an irrational dislike to my personal assistant? Why didn't you trust me?'

'But don't you see, Luke, that's the whole problem,' she exclaimed angrily. 'How was I supposed to trust you, when you gave me so little of yourself? The only time I shared your life was during those awful, formal dinner parties, and a few hours at night—if and when you weren't too involved with business meetings.'

'Nothing in life is that black and white, Samantha,' he said slowly. 'I'll admit that maybe I was over-preoccupied with work, but some of the problems in our marriage certainly weren't my fault. For instance, you expected me to look after you, just as your father had done, but I wanted a wife—not a spoilt child.'

'I wasn't spoilt—that's a rotten thing to say!'

'But true,' he insisted, raising himself to look down at her. 'Whenever I made an attempt to explain the harsh facts of life, you would retire into a fit of the sulks. You expected me to run your life for you, to make every single decision...in fact, as far as I could see, you were quite content to have exchanged one father-figure for another.'

'No...that's not right. I didn't...I mean...' Her voice faltered as she gazed up into his quizzical eyes. 'OK, I guess you could be right,' she sighed. 'But that merely underlines the problem. Goodness knows why you married me, Luke, but if I ever wanted a father-figure, I certainly don't want one now.'

'I'm pleased to hear it,' he drawled. 'It wasn't a role that I enjoyed being forced to play,' he added with a mocking grin as he ran a finger lightly down the side of her face.

She could feel her heart beginning to pound at his soft touch. 'Yes, well...the fact is, we didn't have enough between us on which to base any sort of relationship, let alone a marriage. Which is all the more reason for you to give me a divorce,' she said breathlessly, desperately trying to control her wayward mind. But it was proving difficult to ignore the hand now trailing down over her neck, and gently caressing the hollows at the base of her throat. 'And...and you must see that we...we were totally unsuited and...and incompatible?'

'I would have said that there was one, very important aspect of our married life, in which we were thoroughly compatible!'

'No, Luke!' she gasped as his hands began moving slowly over her body. 'I—I thought you said that you had some...some other plans for this afternoon?'

'Oh, yes—indeed I do!' he drawled, the gleam in his eyes and the explicit touch of the fingers caressing her full breast making his intentions quite plain.

'But...but, this isn't the answer...'

'I'm not interested in answers—or questions for that matter.' His soft, mocking voice seemed to echo in her ears as he moved his body to trap her beneath him, once more. 'Only in the total certainty that you want me, every bit as much as I want you.'

'No,' she gasped. 'No—let me go!'

'Like hell I will,' he muttered huskily as his dark head came down towards her.

Other than their brief encounters following his arrival on the island, it was four years since she had been in his arms. But from the moment his mouth hungrily claimed hers, parting her lips with savage intensity, all the past days, months and years seemed to vanish as if they had never been. The stark impact of his rampant desire, the force of his kiss and the hands sweeping down over her body to brush aside her gown, was a potent reminder that the physical bond between them had always been a compelling force, sufficiently strong to melt all her resistance, even during the most unhappy days of her marriage. Now, as then, she found herself being swept inexorably along on a fast tide of rising passion and desire, instinctively responding to the heavy pressure of his body against hers, the shivering excitement of his warm hands on her bare skin.

And then the hard, demanding possession of his mouth slowly softened, gently bewitching and beguiling her senses, and bringing her to a shocking awareness and belated realisation of her true feelings. She now knew, with every fibre of her being, that she didn't want him to stop. The truth was that she *wanted* to feel his lips on hers, the touch of his hands on her body... and that she had wanted it, with increasing desperation, ever since he had arrived on the island.

'You want me—don't you, Samantha?' His hoarse voice seemed to echo her own distraught thoughts as he raised his head to look at the girl lying dazed in his arms, his lips parting in a slow, sensual smile as he gazed down at her confused, bewildered expression. And then he lowered his head to kiss the pulse throbbing at the base of her throat.

Samantha moaned, a sharp thrill of pure, physical pleasure exploding inside her at the downward path of his mouth, the exquisite excitement and the deep, aching need for fulfilment as his lips closed over first one swollen nipple and then the other.

'Tell me...' he whispered thickly against her flesh. 'Tell me that you want me...'

'Oh, God! Yes—yes, I want you,' she gasped helplessly, oblivious to everything but a driving, imperative need to succumb to the wanton desires of her own body, the compulsive urge to surrender to the increasingly erotic, sexually explicit touch of his mouth and hands.

Luke gave a deep groan, swiftly tearing off his clothes, and then lifting her like a doll as he ripped away her thin gown before tossing her back against the pillows. There was nothing gentle or tender in their lovemaking. They both seemed possessed by a savagely raw, emotional hunger which had been repressed for too long, passion exploding between them as their bodies merged in a fiercely wild, untamed consummation. Drowning in ecstasy, Samantha was scarcely aware of repeatedly crying out his name, the breath rasping in her throat as she eagerly yielded to the thrusting possession of his powerful body, his heart thudding and pounding against hers as they both fell shuddering into a deep, dark abyss of mutual joy and satisfaction.

Much later, as they lay drowsily replete, Samantha was just drifting off to sleep when she found herself being forced back into reality. Still dazed by the overwhelming passion which had flared between them, and incredulous at the force of her own response to Luke's frenzied, hungry possession, it was some moments before she managed to drag herself up to the surface of full consciousness. Oh, God! *What had she done?* As she gazed at Luke's recumbent form in dawning horror, her body writhing with ever-increasing shame and self-disgust, it became slowly borne in upon her that she hadn't been disturbed solely by a bad conscience. Wasn't that...? She was sure she'd heard something...? A heavy crash as the front door was thrown open confirmed her worst fears. Someone was entering the sugar mill!

'Sam? Hello, Samantha? Where are you?'

It was Gerald! She'd completely and utterly forgotten that he'd said he was coming over to St Pauls this afternoon. Oh—oh, help! *What on earth was she going to do now?*

CHAPTER SIX

DAZED and stunned as she was by Gerald's sudden appearance, it was a moment or two before Samantha managed to collect her scattered wits. And then the sound of his voice calling her name as he looked into the small kitchen below quickly galvanised her drowsy, lethargic body into action. Scrambling off the bed, she grabbed the corner of a sheet, frantically tugging it from beneath Luke's comatose figure and wrapping it hurriedly around herself, before staggering across to the balcony which overlooked the room below.

'Oh, h-hello, Gerald...' she croaked huskily, her pale cheeks surrounded by a flame-like halo of tangled curls as she gazed down at the upturned face of the handsome, fair-haired Englishman. 'I...um...I forgot that you were coming today, and...well, I guess I...er...I must have fallen asleep...'

'That's OK.' Gerald beamed up at her. 'I must say, you look really fantastic! Shall I come up and join you?' he added hopefully.

'*No!*' she gasped breathlessly. 'I mean...I...' She closed her eyes for a moment as she tried to control her trembling figure, desperately hunting through her numb, sluggish mind for an answer to the predicament in which she now found herself. 'I'm very tired...and...um...well, Gerald, the fact is...'

'The fact is—darling Samantha isn't receiving visitors today,' a voice drawled from behind her shoulder. 'Maybe you should come back another time?'

Samantha's eyes glazed with horror and she gave a helpless moan, slumping against the wooden rail of the balcony as she turned to see Luke walking over to smile blandly down at the Englishman.

'Who...? What...? Who's that? And what's he doing up in your b-bedroom?' Gerald stuttered, growing red in the face as he pointed an angry, shaking finger up at Luke.

'For God's sake!' Samantha hissed urgently. But her detestable husband clearly didn't intend to take a blind bit of notice of anything she said.

'Tsk, tsk.' Luke shook his head in mock sorrow. 'Really, Gerald, old boy, you seem to be a bit slow on the uptake,' he drawled in an atrocious English accent.

'Oh—Samantha!'

'Oh—God!'

'Oh—dear!' Luke murmured, before he burst out laughing at the deep, heartfelt groans of dismay issuing from both his wife and her boyfriend.

Samantha whirled on him, trembling with fury. 'Shut up! Shut up—you rat!'

'There's no need to scream at me like a fishwife!' The Englishman bristled angrily.

'I didn't mean *you*, Gerald,' she moaned helplessly.

'And I certainly don't deserve to be treated in this way. How was I to know that you were *that* sort of woman?' he added in a high-pitched aggrieved tone of voice. 'I never dreamed...'

'Just a minute!' she snapped, frowning down at the man below. 'What do you mean by "that sort of woman"? This is my husband, for heaven's sake!'

'Oh, yes?' he sneered.

'Yes—of course he is.'

'Humph! This is the first I've heard about any so-called husband!' Gerald gave an angry laugh as he glared up at Luke.

'But it's true!' Samantha wailed, almost dancing with frustration and convinced that she was in the midst of some appalling nightmare. 'Oh, for goodness' sake, Luke, will you please tell Gerald that we really are married?'

Luke shook his head sorrowfully. 'But you're always telling me that we're *not* really married...' he said with a heavy, dramatic sigh.

Struggling with the thick sheet enveloping her figure, Samantha's bellow of rage was abruptly terminated as Luke calmly picked her up and tossed her carelessly back on to the bed.

'I sure go for a woman with spirit!' he laughed, returning to grin down at the Englishman, whose fury had temporarily given way to a puzzled, angry frown.

'Hang on—I've seen you before, haven't I?' Gerald muttered. 'Let me see...in Antigua...last month, wasn't it?' He snapped his fingers. 'Yes, of course—that's it! You were coming out of my lawyer's office. And now I come to think of it...he told me, just the other day, that he had an American client who was thinking of buying this hotel from old Emily Ward. So, *that's* what you're doing here.'

'Well, no—not entirely old boy...' Luke drawled. 'Believe me, this little lady is really hot stuff!' He winked down at the Englishman, his eyes gleaming with laughter as he struggled to keep a straight face.

'You...you *evil bastard*!' Samantha yelled, fighting to free herself from the sheet, and gibbering with rage as she contemplated the great pleasure—not to say deep, *deep* satisfaction—of blackening Luke's other eye.

'Hot stuff...?' Gerald's cheeks had taken on a livid, purple hue, and it looked as if he was going to explode at any moment. 'I don't normally associate with loose women!' He gave a jeering, scornful laugh.

'I heard that!' Samantha cried, finally managing to free herself. 'How *dare* you call me a loose woman?' she shouted furiously. 'Get out of here you...*you louse!*'

'Don't worry—I'm going!' he shouted as he hurried towards the exit. 'And as far as I'm concerned, it's good riddance to bad rubbish!'

Following the loud crash as the front door was slammed shut with considerable force, a long silence descended on the sugar mill. Feeling totally exhausted, Samantha rewound the sheet about her trembling figure, staring at her husband who was leaning over the balcony, doubled up with laughter.

'OK, Luke,' she said as his mirth began to subside. 'I've certainly got to hand it to you—*old boy*. That was a really good performance you've just put on.'

'Oh, God—I haven't laughed so much in years!' His tall frame was shaken by another peal of hilarious laughter.

'That's good, because now you've had your fun—you can get out of here,' she said grimly. 'Out of here...and out of my life—*permanently!*'

'Aw, come on, sweetheart,' he grinned. 'You know I was only kidding.'

'Kidding...?' she echoed bitterly. 'If you think that I'm likely to be amused by your Oscar-winning act, just now, you're going to have to think again!'

'Face facts, Samantha—I did you a big favour,' he said crisply. 'That guy was a real wimp—one of the dregs of humanity, for God's sake! Even if I was prepared to tolerate any man fooling around with my wife—which

I certainly am not!—he was absolutely the wrong person for you. Surely you must see that?'

Samantha sighed heavily and went over to stare out of the window. 'What I do see is that while I may have been blind and stupid these last few days, there's nothing wrong with my hearing.' She turned around, her eyes dazed with pain as she watched him getting dressed. 'You are buying the hotel, as Gerald said, aren't you? It all makes sense now,' she added, pushing a trembling hand through her long red hair. 'Corrine—who's obviously the architect for the new hotel; the way you've been examining the fabric and structure of the buildings; how you knew about Aunt Emily's operation. And why not—since you've obviously been negotiating secretly together. You never could resist a good business deal, could you, Luke?' she added scornfully.

'It's not like that.'

'Oh, no?' She gave a derisory laugh. 'Aunt Emily may be old, but *I've* still got my wits about me. Don't tell me that you aren't picking up a prime piece of property dead cheap, because I won't believe you.'

'You're wrong,' he retorted curtly. 'I'm paying a very fair price—considerably over the odds, in fact. And you know very well that I would never cheat your aunt,' he added, moving across the floor towards her. 'Emily will be glad to retire from a job that's become too much for her to cope with, and now she'll be able to live in comfort for the rest of her life.'

'It sounds as if it's just one of your usual typically clever deals!' Samantha groaned out angrily. 'I haven't forgotten your favourite business maxim: divide and rule. And that is exactly what you've done, isn't it? You've very sneakily kept the whole thing a secret from me— since you knew I'd never agree—and all the while you've been dangling your money bags in front of a confused old woman.'

Luke's hands gripped her slim shoulders, his tense fingers biting into her flesh. 'That simply isn't true,' he said angrily. 'It was your aunt who contacted me, and not the other way round.'

'I don't believe it! She'd never...'

'Oh, yes, she did,' he grated. 'We've been in constant touch with each other during these past years, and Emily knew that one of my companies has recently taken over the Prestige Hotels chain. She also knew that I had decided to sell off some hotels, and to concentrate on sites with a superb location—such as the one here, on St Pauls—with a view to offering total luxury for those who can afford it. She approached me in the first instance, and it has taken me some months to finally agree to purchase this place. And do you know why?' he added grimly.

'No, I...'

'Because Emily, far from being the "confused old woman" you seem to fondly imagine her to be, is in fact a double-dealing, rapacious old trout, who would skin me alive if I gave her half a chance!' He gave a grim snort of sardonic laughter. 'Not only am I going to have to spend a fortune on doing up this ramshackle place, but your dear old aunt has also bargained for an extremely large capital sum, in addition to the purchase price of the hotel. Heaven knows, I may not be too happy about the deal, but at least you must be pleased to know that Emily is now going to have an easy, comfortable life?'

'Yes—yes, of course I am. But what about *my* life?' Samantha demanded. 'It's obvious that while you and Aunt Emily have been plotting so happily together, neither of you has bothered to give a damn about the fact that I'm going to lose the only home I've got. And that's not all, is it?' she added with harsh bitterness. 'There's nothing like a little dalliance to pass the time while you've been sewing up the deal, right? Congratulations, Luke—it looks as if you've taken all the tricks in this particular game, doesn't it?'

'Don't be such a damn fool!' he rasped, his eyes cold and hard, a muscle throbbing in his clenched jaw. 'Yes, I'm buying the hotel from your aunt—and yes, I'll admit it will be a good business investment—eventually. But if you think I made love to you just for kicks—or for a cheap thrill,' he shook her fiercely, 'then you *really* must be very blind and totally, utterly stupid!'

Trembling with rage, he pushed her away and she stumbled over the length of sheet still wrapped about her figure, suddenly frightened by the expression on his face. She couldn't remember ever having seen him looking so angry or ferocious before, and she backed nervously away as he advanced menacingly towards her.

'My patience has finally run out,' he snarled. 'You may as well know that your aunt has already signed all the papers, and I now own this hotel. There's no place for you here, Samantha,' he added brutally. 'And so, when I return to the States, you...' he jabbed a finger in her chest, 'you are coming with me!'

'Never!'

'Never say never, sweetheart,' he whispered savagely through clenched teeth, jerking her into his arms and crushing her against him as he possessed her mouth in a hard, forceful kiss. She struggled, trying to avoid his savage lips, but then his kiss altered, growing soft and seductive, coaxing her lips apart. To her deep chagrin and shame she found herself weakening, helpless to prevent her instinctive response to his powerful mastery of her emotions as she buried her fingers in his dark hair, curving her body even closer to his.

When he lifted his head, she slowly opened her dazed eyes and shivered at the cold, triumphant smile on his lips. Roughly sweeping aside the sheet from her quivering, shaking figure, he continued to hold her in a firm grip with one hand, as he slowly and sensually caressed her body with the other. '*This* is why you'll be coming back to the States with me,' he said, his voice heavy with cruel mockery as she trembled helplessly beneath the soft, erotic touch of his fingers on her bare flesh. 'And don't even begin to think of running away again. Because this time, I'm not prepared to let you go,' he threatened grimly, abruptly pushing her away, so that she staggered and fell back on to the bed as he strode off towards the staircase. 'Believe me, I'll follow you to the ends of the earth, if necessary!'

Throttling back the engines to maintain a steady cruising speed, Samantha called up air-traffic control in Antigua to give her course and altitude, before settling back into her seat. The morning sun was rising fast now, the same fiery red ball that had provided such a spectacular sunset last night. The guests had been entranced by the sight, but she felt strangely uneasy about the unusually still, calm air and the way the sea over which she was flying seemed to be as flat as a mill pond.

It's just tension, she told herself roughly. The nervous strain which she had been suffering for the past few days would have been enough to give anyone the shakes, and the shock of the sudden confrontation earlier this morning had just about been the last straw.

She'd already made up her mind to take off for St Barts this morning, and Luke's threat yesterday had merely reinforced her determination to leave the island—

and the hotel—as soon as possible. She had to check up on the problems with her shop, of course, but it was also imperative that she saw Aunt Emily. However, after spending much of yesterday evening trying to get a call through to the hospital, with absolutely no success whatever, she had decided to go first to St Barts, and then to fly back to Antigua later on this afternoon.

All through the long hours of a disturbed and restless night, she had alternately swung between a strong urge to strangle her deceitful old aunt—and the acknowledgement that the sale of the hotel would relieve Aunt Emily of all financial anxiety, and provide her with a comfortable retirement. There wasn't any choice, of course. Samantha knew that, if only for the older woman's sake, she'd have to go along with Luke's new scheme for the hotel—although she was heartsick at the prospect of losing the only real home she had ever known.

Maybe she was running away again, she thought gloomily, but she knew that she was desperately vulnerable as far as Luke was concerned. His lovemaking yesterday, and the way she had succumbed so quickly and so completely, only demonstrated how susceptible she was; how pathetically weak and defenceless against the power of his overwhelming, sensual attraction. When he touched her... Samantha sighed, trying to ignore the quick spasm of excitement which flared through her body—a longing that no amount of cool reason could dispel. When she was near him, she seemed to lose all power of judgement and logic, completely forgetting her past, unhappy life with the ruthless businessman who had proved to be such a neglectful husband. It followed, therefore, that to remain in the hotel, even for the next few days, would be a recipe for disaster—especially with Luke breathing down her neck every five seconds. And as for his threat to take her back to that grim apartment in New York...even the thought was enough to make her shake with fear.

How could she have possibly guessed the lengths to which Luke would go? What a rat the man was! she told herself grimly, glancing back over her shoulder and glaring at the two passengers in the rear of the aeroplane. 'Stowaways' was a better word, she thought, her green eyes flashing with angry frustration as they swept over the figures of Luke and Corrine, who were busy looking at a thick pile of architectural blueprints.

The shock of finding her husband and his companion in the small airport building, earlier this morning, had left her utterly speechless for a few moments. 'Wh-what are you doing here?' she had gasped when she'd eventually managed to find her voice.

'We're going to St Barts—with you, sweetheart,' Luke had drawled. 'And before you start causing a rumpus, I'd better tell you that while I know it's your aunt's plane, I'm damn sure you don't have her *written* authorisation for its use, hmm? And so, if you don't take us with you— I'll inform the authorities, here, that you've stolen the plane.'

'Nonsense! They know me. They...they'd never believe you!'

'Do you really want to try and find out—the hard way?' he asked, his voice as smooth as silk.

Opening her mouth, and just about to tell him to go to hell, she paused for a second before lapsing back into a frustrated silence. No, she didn't want to go through all the hassle that would undoubtedly ensue if Luke tried to make trouble. Not that the matter wouldn't be sorted out in her favour—eventually. But she certainly didn't relish the thought of standing around this small airport for most of the day.

He really was the pits! she thought, glaring up at him
with stormy eyes. And, what was more, it was *absolutely maddening* to see that the damned man had—lord
knew how—managed to avoid getting the black eye
which had looked yesterday as if it was developing in
such a thoroughly satisfactory manner. But now she was
cruelly disappointed to note, as she stared up into his
handsome face, that there was only a small bruise at the
corner of his eye. What a swine the man was!

'You damn blackmailer!' she hissed with fury. 'Who
told you I was flying to St Barts? Was it Penny? How
did you manage to worm it out of her?'

'With my fascinating charm and wonderfully exciting
personality, darling. What else?' he murmured with a
broad, infuriating grin.

Controlling herself with difficulty, Samantha forced
herself to count to ten, before she said through gritted
teeth, 'OK, I know when I'm over a barrel, you louse!'
before striding off to get the plane out of the hangar.
'There is just one thing,' she added as Corrine and Luke
settled into their seats before take-off. 'I don't know if
either of you two, "wonderfully exciting" people have
flown into St Barts before, but my advice...'

'When we want your advice, we'll ask for it, Mrs
Brandon!' Corrine had snapped irritably as she did up
her seat-belt. 'Some of us have actually flown in private
planes before, you know.'

OK, Miss high-and-mighty...on your own head be
it! Samantha had mouthed silently to herself as she continued with the pre-flight checks.

Although, now, as she contacted air traffic on St
Martin, which controlled the passage of aeroplanes for
all the nearby small islands, she still had no idea why
Corrine should be in such a foul, sarcastic mood. But
as Samantha received instructions on the speed and, more

importantly, the direction of the wind, she was quite sure that the next few minutes would—hopefully!—disturb the other girl's irritatingly cool composure.

If Corrine had been prepared to listen, Samantha would have told her that St Jean airport on St Barthélemy—or St Barts as it was known throughout the Caribbean—possessed a runway that was guaranteed to sort out the men from the boys; and that, like every other local pilot, she had been required to gain a special certificate before being allowed to land on the island.

However, while Samantha was concentrating on her final preparations for descent, Corrine was gazing down at the green fields and blue lagoons, sparkling in the early morning sun. She was just wondering how long it would be before she sighted the airport, when she looked up to see that they appeared to be flying directly towards—into?—a large, tree-covered mountain. Eyes dilated with horror, she briefly noted the hardly reassuring sight of a large, white stone cross as the plane skimmed over the mountain top, and then there was a sudden, deathly silence. *Oh, my God!* That dangerous, raving lunatic sitting in the pilot's seat—she . . . she'd cut the engines of the aircraft!

'We're going to die! Your damned wife is going to kill us . . . !' Corrine shrieked in terror, frantically grabbing Luke's arm, drumming her heels, and continuing to scream at the top of her voice as the aircraft seemed to plunge down into a bottomless void. She was still screeching hysterically as Samantha gently glided the aeroplane down on to the concrete runway, to make a perfect three-point landing.

'Oh, dear, oh, dear! Poor Corrine doesn't look too well, does she?' Samantha drawled callously some minutes later, watching as the other girl stumbled down the steps, swearing at her employer's wife in a thoroughly unladylike manner, before staggering off towards the airport building. 'Still—you seem to be in fairly good shape,' she murmured, glancing sideways at Luke who, apart from a slightly pale face, seemed remarkably unaffected by their unorthodox landing.

'Why not? Would you be disappointed if I told you I had perfect confidence in your flying ability?' he enquired blandly, although she noticed that his dark eyebrows were raised as he gazed at the short runway, which was bounded by the sea at one end, and a tall mountain at the other.

'However, I hope you're going to have the decency to apologise to poor Corrine,' he continued sternly. 'You might at least have warned her...'

'I did try—but your girlfriend wasn't prepared to listen,' Samantha protested as he took a firm grip on her arm and began leading her across the tarmac.

'If you refer to her as my "girlfriend" once more— I'll kill you!' he growled threateningly, his stride lengthening so that she had to run to keep up with him.

'Hey, let me go!' she panted breathlessly.

'No, there's someone I want you to meet. Ah, there she is!' he exclaimed, a warm smile breaking out on his face as he waved to a girl standing in a fenced off enclosure.

'It's not...yes—it is! *Barbara!*' she called out excitedly, twisting out of his grip to run over and greet the friend she hadn't seen for so long. Chatting nineteen to the dozen, she was eventually hauled away by Luke to go through the brief entry formalities, before being reunited with his sister.

'Isn't this terrific! I knew my dear brother was coming over to see us some time, but I didn't know until late last night that it would be today!' Barbara laughed happily, leading the way out of the airport building towards the car park. 'Hey! How about my *"voiture"*?' she giggled, waving her arms in a flamboyant gesture towards a red mini-moke, topped by a scarlet and white stripped canvas awning which served as the roof of the vehicle.

'For God's sake—I'll never be able to get in there.' Luke gave a wry laugh as he surveyed the small car, which looked ridiculously tiny beside his tall figure.

'Tough luck!' Barbara retorted crisply. 'It's bigger than it looks, but if you can't make it—well, you'll just have to run behind us, won't you?'

Still in her flying suit, Samantha had no difficulty in climbing into the back seat, her lips widening in a grin as she listened to her husband and his young sister, who were amicably trading insults with one another as he discovered there was plenty of room for his rangy, long-legged frame in the front passenger seat of the mini. It was clear that Barbara was well able to cope with Luke's strong personality. And it was equally obvious that he enjoyed being teased, responding to his sister's mild bullying and jocular, scathing comments with dry amusement as he leaned over to give her a warm kiss on the cheek.

As they drove out of the small airport complex, Samantha became increasingly oblivious to her surroundings. Ignoring Barbara's bright chatter, and the stiff, angry figure of Corrine who was sitting beside her, she stared blindly out at the passing scenery.

It was as if she had been hit by a thunderbolt, or a sudden blow to the solar plexus—her mind a seething mass of conflicting emotions as she tried to come to terms with a startling reassessment of her husband's character. She was shattered by the realisation that, by failing to credit Luke with either kindness or a sense of humour—

both of which he clearly possessed—she had been guilty of looking down the wrong end of the telescope: *a truly massive case of tunnel vision.* Could that have been one of the main reasons why their marriage had gone so swiftly on the rocks? she wondered unhappily. If... if she hadn't been so in awe of Luke, when they had first been married, maybe she might have seen him as he really was—not only a tough, ruthless businessman, but also someone who was capable of warmth and tenderness.

'...and so Edmond hired this terrific little car for me. Wasn't that sweet of him?' Barbara asked, turning to smile at Samantha who was sitting in the back of the vehicle, beside an equally silent Corrine.

'Hmm...?' Samantha blinked with confusion.

'For heaven's sake, Barbara—keep your eye on the road!' Luke warned urgently as they only just missed an on-coming vehicle.

'Oh, pooh! Stop being such an old fuss-pot,' his sister laughed, driving at what seemed break-neck speed down the road towards Gustavia, the capital of St Barts. 'I'm really crazy about this island—once I'd got over our arrival, that is. Oh, boy! How you have the nerve to fly one of those tiny planes, Samantha, let alone landing the damn thing on that *really* frightening runway, certainly beats me!'

Samantha smiled, her explanation that it wasn't half as dangerous as it looked not quite masking Corrine's moans of distress at being reminded, once again, of what was clearly one of the most frightening moments of her life.

'St Barts is really great,' Barbara added, continuing her blithely erratic progress through the streets of the old town. 'It's as French as could be, but until the mid-nineteenth century it belonged to Sweden. That's really one strange mixture—but it seems to work, because this place is absolute heaven.'

Luke grinned. 'There's no need to bore Samantha with a potted history of the island, because she's got a boutique, here in Gustavia.'

'No kidding?'

'Umm…yes…' Samantha murmured, wondering how on earth Luke knew about her shop. 'Could you please drop me off in the Rue du Général de Gaulle?' she asked.

'But I thought you were going to have lunch with us?' Barbara wailed.

'Don't panic—she is.'

'Oh, I am, am I?' Samantha drawled, her hackles rising.

'Yes, you are,' Luke said firmly. 'I'll pick you up at one o'clock.'

She longed to say no, but she realised that, however much satisfaction she might get in giving Luke a sharp set-down, it would mean losing the opportunity of renewing her friendship with his sister.

'Oh—all right,' she sighed as the car slowed down. 'I'll see you later, Barbara. 'Bye,' she called, as she climbed out of the vehicle, waiting until it had driven away before walking across the road towards a smart boutique.

Samantha spent a useful morning in the shop, managing to sort out all the difficulties facing Janina, the manageress, whom she'd congratulated on a very successful month's trading figures. From the first, Samantha had operated a simple system whereby all the staff in her boutiques were entitled to a small percentage of the profits on top of their salary, and both she and her manageress had been very satisfied with the morning's stocktaking. She hadn't realised just how fast the time had flown when Janina came into the small office and, with a broad smile on her face, announced that a tall, handsome man—*'aussi beau qu'une vedette'*, she added with a wink—had arrived and was asking for her.

'As good-looking as a film star, indeed!' Samantha muttered grimly, knowing full well who it was as she gathered up her purse and flying suit, before going through into the showroom.

She found Luke strolling casually around the boutique, looking about him with curiosity. 'This is a really very impressive, and I particularly admire the décor,' he murmured, not bothering to disguise his surprise as he glanced at the display cases lined with royal blue silk, providing such a spectacular backcloth to the shimmering crystal goblets; and the discreet lighting which cleverly emphasised the deep, rich glow of the gold and silver jewellery.

Although she was aware of feeling a nervous mass of complex, tangled emotions about her husband, and was also somewhat apprehensive about the forthcoming lunch with Barbara and her new husband, Samantha couldn't help smiling at Luke's expression of puzzlement and confusion as he gazed about his luxurious surroundings.

'It's very... it's not at all...'

'What you expected?' She gave a low, wry laugh. 'Out of sheer interest—what *did* you expect? Some tacky little shop selling secondhand clothes?'

'No, not exactly,' he drawled with sardonic amusement. 'But I have to confess that I certainly didn't believe it would prove to be quite so glamorous. Are all your other shops like this?'

'Yes—all five of them.'

'Hmm...' He gazed down at the thick carpet, clearly deep in thought.

'Don't bother trying to do the sums, Luke,' she told him sharply. 'I know exactly what you're thinking! Yes, I've built up a nice little capital investment—but I've had to work extremely hard, and have *no* intention of selling out and going back to the States with you!' She glared at him defiantly. 'And just in case you're wondering, I can tell you that I hold all the shares in this small company—so you can just keep your sticky fingers well away from my business!'

He laughed, taking her arm as he led her out into the street. 'You're a clever girl,' he said, opening the passenger door of his sister's car. 'In fact,' he added, as he came around and settled himself into the driving seat, 'I'm very proud of both you and what you've achieved in such a relatively short space of time.'

'Wow! Be still, my beating heart!' she muttered caustically, although she couldn't help feeling a deep glow of satisfaction. Coming from that successful business tycoon, Luke Brandon, such words were praise indeed. However, she had a far more pressing matter on her mind, and one that she ought to get sorted out as soon as possible.

'I want to see Barbara, and catch up on all her news,' Samantha said as he drove out of the town. 'But when I took off this morning, I wasn't expecting to go anywhere smart and, as you can see, there's no way I'm dressed for a lunch party.' She gestured helplessly at her white cotton slacks and tight-fitting, navy blue T-shirt.

Luke gave her a sideways grin. 'Relax. I'm crazy about your T-shirt,' he murmured, gazing appreciatively at her full breasts.

'Ha, ha,' she muttered sarcastically, cross with herself for not being able to control the flush spreading over her cheeks. 'It's all very well for you,' she grumbled, glancing at his tan coloured trousers and cream silk shirt, a thin brown leather belt and gold buckle emphasising his slim waist. It was absolutely sickening that, whatever the circumstances, he always looked immaculate and—very unfortunately, as far as she was concerned—sensationally attractive.

'There's no need for you to panic,' he said reassuringly. 'We're going to join the others at *Les Castelets* for lunch, and then go back to Edmond's old family home at La Pointe Milou for a swim and...'

'*Les Castelets*...?' she shrieked in alarm. 'Oh, my God—that's absolutely *the* smartest restaurant, and always full of the Parisian jet set! Oh, no...no way...'

Samantha had been so preoccupied with impressing upon Luke that, dressed as she was, she couldn't possibly turn up at such a chic establishment, she hadn't noticed that he had pulled into the side of the road. He swiftly cut the engine, releasing their seat-belts, and before she knew what was happening, she suddenly found herself clasped in his arms. Grasping her chin and tilting her face up towards him, he lowered his dark head until his mouth was poised over hers.

'When will you stop fighting—and learn to trust me?' he murmured.

'No,' she begged desperately. 'No, don't...'

'Kiss you...?' he drawled softly, brushing his mouth across her trembling lips. 'Oh, but I shall—wherever and whenever I wish to do so!'

Samantha *knew* that she ought to struggle, to try and evade the firm, hard grip of his embrace. But it was as if she had become mentally paralysed, staring mesmerised up into his gleaming blue eyes, excitement scorching through her body and her lips parting in a soft invitation as his warm mouth claimed hers.

There was a controlled hunger in the hard body pressed so closely to hers, a fierce possession in the hand that slipped beneath her T-shirt to cup the swollen fullness of her breasts. The touch of his fingers brushing tantalisingly over her taut nipples caused the blood to sing in her ears, and she gave a helpless moan of capitulation, winding her arms up around his neck as his kiss deepened and she surrendered to the erotic pleasure of his lovemaking.

It seemed an age before he slowly raised his head, releasing her from his embrace as he gently trailed a forefinger down her pale cheek, and over her quivering lips. 'So, we are agreed? We will join Barbara and Edmond for lunch, hmm?'

For the life of her, there was nothing she could possibly say. Leaning back in her seat, Samantha closed her eyes. She was feeling far too emotionally exhausted to do more than turn her head away in a vain, hopeless attempt to hide the hectic flush spreading over her face. *I hate him ... I hate him,* she chanted desperately to herself. But, of course—and that was the real problem, wasn't it?—she didn't. Almost fainting with dizziness as she at last began to comprehend the quite appalling, disastrous truth, it was all she could do not to moan out loud with dismay.

Sitting in a ridiculously small car, half-way up a mountain in St Barts, was hardly the best place to discover that, despite all the unhappiness and misery of the past—and after all these years, for heaven's sake!—she was still head over heels in love with her husband!

CHAPTER SEVEN

THE RED mini-moke suddenly turned right, the small vehicle moving on down a narrow, unsignposted road which soon disintegrated into a rough, bumpy track.

'Hey! This isn't the way to *Les Castelets*.' Samantha turned to look accusingly at Luke. 'Where on earth do you think you're going?'

'I'm not entirely sure. However, if I followed the directions correctly, this road should lead us to Gouverneur Beach.'

'But...but that's a good two or three kilometres away from the restaurant!'

'You're quite right, so it is,' Luke agreed with a bland smile.

'Why you—*ah!*' Samantha gasped as they suddenly hit a large pothole. For the next few minutes she was forced to remain silent, clinging on to her seat for dear life as the small car bounced up and down over boulders littering the rough track.

What a fool she was! Samantha fumed, grinding her teeth with angry frustration. She ought to have guessed, when he had insisted on picking her up from the shop, that Luke would have some sneaky, devious plan in mind. After all, she'd always known that when it came to low cunning and guile—Luke could make Machiavelli look like a mere amateur!

'We'll be lucky if we don't get the bottom torn out of this boneshaker!' she grated, continuing to mutter angrily under her breath as they lurched on down the track. Just when she was contemplating taking her life in her hands and jumping out of the car—anything had to be better than suffering this purgatory!—they turned a corner, and Luke brought the vehicle to a halt.

'*Voilà!* as Barbara would say,' he laughed, getting out and stretching his long legs, before coming around to open her door. 'I think this was worth the journey, don't you?' he said, gesturing at the beautiful long stretch of fine, golden sand edged by sparkling blue sea, which appeared to be completely deserted.

'Humph...it's all right, I suppose,' Samantha grumbled, still feeling shaken to bits by her rough jolting, and also struggling to come to terms with the alarming fact that, despite all her efforts, she was still in love with the man standing beside her.

'Don't be so grouchy!'

'I'm not,' she protested.

'Yes, you are—and you can cut it out, right now,' he said firmly, before bending down to remove his shoes and socks.

'But what about Edmond and Barbara? They're expecting us to join them for lunch and...'

'We'll join them later,' Luke assured her. 'There's at least an hour to go before we're expected at the restaurant.'

'But why...'

'For goodness' sake—stop moaning!' he retorted. 'I've brought you here because ever since I arrived in St Pauls, we've never really had the opportunity to be alone together. First your drunken chef, and then your boy-friend—it's been one damn thing after another! Besides, I've got a hankering to explore an old pirate's cave, and look for buried treasure,' he grinned.

Samantha had been just about to give him a piece of her mind—he'd got a nerve talking about her 'boy-friend', because as far as she was concerned, there was still a very large question mark over his relationship with his lady architect—but she found herself staring at him in open-mouthed astonishment instead.

'You? Looking for buried treasure?' she queried in amazement. 'Do you mean a pirate's hoard of gold doubloons and pieces of eight? Like in all those old "yo-ho-ho and a bottle of rum" stories?'

Luke gave her a broad smile. 'Sure, why not? Edmond was telling me that some fierce old French pirate—a guy known as Monbars the Exterminator—buried his secret hoard of gold in a cave on this beach. I thought it might be fun to have a look and see what we can find.'

'Yes, well…' She blinked in confusion. Ye Gods! What on earth had come over the normally suave, sophisticated Luke Brandon?

'Come on,' he said, taking a firm hold of her hand. 'Let's forget we're grown-up, responsible adults—and go treasure-hunting!'

Samantha hesitated for a moment. The very last thing she wanted at this juncture was to find herself alone with Luke. On the other hand, it might be fun to explore an old pirate's cave… 'OK—I'll give it a whirl, but I warn you that I draw the line at having to walk the plank,' she added, grinning at her own childish folly as they began to walk over the warm sand.

Unfortunately, when they reached it, the pirate's cave appeared to be disappointingly bare of all treasure.

'I don't know where old Monbars kept his loot, but he'd have had a hard time burying it in there.' Samantha, sitting on a wide, flat rock outside the cave, nodded towards the large dark opening behind her. 'I reckon the only way of finding out for sure would be to dynamite the stone floor of the cave…and I don't think that treasure-hunting *aficionados* would regard that as quite playing the game!'

'No—I guess not,' Luke muttered absently, staring down into a small rock pool, which was filled with sea water from the receding tide.

Gazing at her husband as he knelt over the pool, a heavy lock of dark hair falling over his eyes, Samantha had a sudden insight of how he must have looked as a young boy. It was only a fleeting vision, but it left her with confused feelings of love and tenderness—something she found acutely disquieting when applied to a man she had always seen as hard, tough and implacable.

'Ah—gotcha!' he suddenly exclaimed, plunging in his hand and laughing as he held up a large crab.

'Watch out! He'll nip your fingers if you're not careful!' she cried anxiously, relieved when Luke smiled and tossed the crab back into the pool.

'It's a shame I can't stay longer on this island,' he said, coming over to sit down beside her. 'Barbara tells me that there's great scuba-diving off the rocks near their house.'

Samantha looked at him in surprise. 'I didn't know you liked diving.'

'I am rapidly coming to the conclusion that there is very little you *do* know about me,' he said quietly, and she flushed as she recalled her disturbing thoughts of a few moments before. 'Before you finally throw in the towel on our marriage,' he continued in the same quiet tone, 'don't you think it might be worth giving it another chance, and maybe discovering that I'm not the black ogre you seem to think I am?'

'No, Luke, I . . . it would never work—not in a million years,' she muttered, staring down at her nervously twisting hands. 'I guess . . . well, in fact, I *know* that I want a great deal more out of life now than I did when I was only eighteen.'

'Such as . . .'

'Just about everything, I guess.' She shrugged. 'I'd like to have a husband whom I saw more than just once or twice a week. In fact, I'd like him to be home every night, if possible. And I want children...and animals...and maybe a house in the country. What I *don't* want is to return to that huge, gloomy apartment of yours—I'd die rather than have to live there again!'

Luke gave an exasperated sigh. 'I wish I knew why on earth you appear to have such a fixation about my old apartment. However, the question is now a purely academic one, since I sold it soon after you left.'

'Really?' She looked at him in surprise. 'So, where are you living now?'

'I've got a penthouse suite with a large roof garden, on Fifth Avenue overlooking Central Park...'

'Goodness! That must have cost you a *fortune*!' she exclaimed.

He shrugged. 'If you don't like it, I can easily find somewhere else. It's people—not places—that are important, Samantha. Surely you know that by now?'

'Yes, of course I do,' she agreed quickly. 'But my dislike of your apartment, however stupid it may seem to you, was all part and parcel of my active dislike of our life-style.' She frowned and brushed a shaking hand through her curly hair. 'I...I wish I knew how to explain it to you, Luke, but while I'm sure that I've changed in the last few years, I don't see any evidence that you have. In fact, as far as I can tell, you're still the same ruthless businessman that you always were. I know...I know,' she said quickly as he opened his mouth to protest. 'As businessmen go, you're terrifically successful—absolutely the greatest!—and I really admire you for what you've done in building up your company until it's now world-famous. But, strange as it may seem, I don't want to be married to Brandon-Phillips

International,' she added, with a helpless shrug of her shoulders. 'I don't want to sit alone, night after night. I don't want to have to learn to be grateful for a few minutes of your valuable time. What I want is an ordinary, everyday husband—not a business tycoon who's so wrapped up in his work that he has no time for anyone or anything, other than what he reads in the *Wall Street Journal*!'

'But I have made considerable changes to my life over the last few years,' he argued, getting to his feet and pacing up and down over the sand. 'I now delegate a great deal of work to my executives; there's the large estate I've bought in East Hampton, and...'

'OK, OK. So you've made a few technical adjustments to your life-style.' She shrugged her shoulders. 'But just as a leopard can't change his spots, I don't see you being able to change what you are: a man who's committed, one hundred per cent, to his business. And let's be honest with one another,' she pleaded. 'It would be unreasonable of me to expect you to turn yourself inside out; to become something you're not. Just as unreasonable, in fact, as the way you expected my share of your life to be limited to occasional entertaining on your behalf, and a few hours alone in bed together,' she added bitterly.

'That's not true—I did no such thing!' he exploded, before taking a deep breath and walking over to stare blindly down into the rock pool. 'Look, I know I wasn't exactly the most brilliant of husbands,' he said at last in a calmer tone of voice. 'In fact, as it turned out, it seems as if I made a thorough mess of the job, right?'

'Well...' Samantha paused. 'If I'm honest, I'd have to say that it takes two to make a mess of things. I was only eighteen, Luke. I'd hardly even begun to stand on my own two feet, and I guess those twelve years between

us were just too large a gap for either of us to handle.
I simply didn't have the sophistication to cope with your
relationship with Adele, for instance.'

'Adele!' Luke swore savagely. 'I might have known
you'd bring that damned woman into the discussion!'
He walked back to stand staring down at her. 'Why
couldn't you have trusted me? Why—when our lovemaking was the only part of our marriage that clearly
did work—why on earth should I have wanted to take
a mistress?'

'You mean...'

'I mean that it's about time you grew up!' he thundered angrily. 'You've spent the last few days telling me
that you've changed, that you're now so much older and
wiser than you were when we were first married. But I
have to tell you that I can see very little evidence of that
fact!'

'You always were blind as a bat—especially if there
was anything you didn't want to see!' she retorted furiously. 'Let me tell you...'

'Oh, no—that's *my* line!' he snarled. 'Let me tell you
a few harsh facts of life. Such as: it's time you woke up,
and realised that you can't spend the rest of your life
existing in some sort of cloud-cuckoo land, hiding away
on a small Caribbean island because you're afraid of life
in the outside world.'

Samantha jumped to her feet. 'I'm not "hiding from
life"!' she shouted, almost dancing with rage.

'Oh, yes, you are,' he remarked flatly. 'You own and
run five successful shops on the various islands out here,
right?'

'Right!' she ground out through clenched teeth.

'You've kept that ramshackle hotel of your aunt's
running—God knows how!—and the constant ups and
downs with the staff, not to mention the problems of

cash-flow for their wages, which must have made it a nightmare to cope with . . . ?'

'Right again!'

'So—maybe you can explain why such a smart, clever lady should be so absolutely and totally convinced that she can't perform the simple task of managing her husband?'

She gave a scornful laugh. 'There's nothing "simple" about you. You're the most complicated person I've ever come across.'

'Nonsense!' he retorted curtly. 'Any woman worth her salt knows how to manage a man—in fact, most of them could do it with one hand tied behind their back! I'll admit that I can be difficult to live with . . .'

'Impossible, you mean!'

'. . . But if you had any spunk or gumption, you'd have regarded life with me as a challenge,' he continued, ignoring her caustic interjection. 'Instead of which, you ran away and have kept your head firmly buried in the sand ever since. And it's no use trying to convince me that the failure of our marriage lies with Adele Francis,' he added coldly. 'If you really believed she was coming between us, then the answer lay in your own hands. You've always had the key to our relationship—I've never understood why you didn't use it to unlock the door.'

Samantha stood goggling at him for a moment, feeling as though she had been hit by a sandbag as she struggled to comprehend what he was saying. 'That . . . that's just about the most chauvinistic rubbish I've ever heard!' she spluttered. 'Are you seriously trying to tell me you think that . . . that a good physical relationship is what marriage is all about?'

'Not entirely. Having trust in one another is also very important.'

'Really? But you didn't trust me, Luke, did you? You didn't trust me enough to let me grow up, to have any thoughts or opinions of my own. I was expected to make a quantum leap of twelve years—all in the space of a few months—and to suddenly be as mature and experienced as you were.' Her eyes flashed with anger. 'And when I proved to be a grievous disappointment, you became impatient and intolerant, completely destroying what little confidence I had.'

'I've already said that I know I made mistakes in the past,' he conceded. 'But that's four years ago, and you're a different person now. Very different,' he murmured, taking a step forward and clasping her in his arms.

Caught completely by surprise, it was a second or two before she began struggling to free herself, and by then it was almost too late. She could feel her bones melting beneath the erotic touch of his hands as they slowly caressed her body, the rising excitement in her veins as his mouth possessed her lips and crushed them hungrily beneath his own. But, even as his kiss deepened, her mind was filled with dark, bitter resentment. Summoning all her strength, she pushed him away, wriggling out from beneath his embrace.

'That's *not* the answer!' she panted, glaring at him defiantly. 'Making love is not going to cure all our problems.'

'No, perhaps not. But it's definitely a start in the right direction,' he said drily.

'Well, it isn't a direction in which I wish to go,' she said firmly. 'I'm not running away, or hiding, or any of the other mistaken ideas you have about me. I simply don't believe that you are capable of being anything other than a complete workaholic. As far as I'm concerned, it's an addiction, every bit as bad as compulsive gambling or alcoholism—and I want none of it!'

He stood staring intently down at her for a moment. 'And that's your final word?' he asked, his voice empty of all expression.

'Yes,' Samantha muttered huskily, unable to understand why she should suddenly be feeling quite so sick and tearful. 'Yes, I want a divorce—and as soon as possible!'

Following Barbara along the marble floor of the wide corridor, Samantha paused as her friend opened a door and led the way into one of the largest, most sumptuous bedrooms that she had ever seen.

'*Voilà!*' Barbara laughed. 'What do you reckon to all this?'

'Good lord!' Samantha's eyes widened in startled amazement at the sight of the enormous, Louis the Sixteenth bed, set up high on a dais and garlanded in yards and yards of deep crimson satin. 'Well—er—it's all very...' Words failed her as her gaze travelled over the mass of heavily ornamented furniture, the many chandeliers which seemed to cover the entire ceiling, and the complicated and intricately designed curtains, the same strong colour as those ornamenting the bed, which were looped and swathed in mad profusion over the tall windows.

'It's really, really terrible, isn't it?' Barbara grinned. 'In fact, it's *so* awful that I'm absolutely crazy about it! This house used to belong to Edmond's grandfather,' she added, going over to sit on the bed. 'And this room was used by his *terrifically* expensive mistress. As soon as we arrived here, I told my darling husband that we simply had to use it ourselves.'

'Oh, Barbara—you are an idiot! You haven't changed a bit!' Samantha couldn't help laughing at her friend's bizarre sense of humour. But in reality, after her trip to

Gouverneur Beach with Luke *and* that awful lunch, she felt more like bursting into tears.

'You haven't changed either, Sam . . . well, not really. I mean, I was so thrilled when Luke said that you and he were getting together again. And although it's plain to see that you're a far more confident, assertive character than you used to be, you're still . . .'

'Look—there seems to be some mistake,' Samantha said quickly. 'I'm not . . . that is, Luke and I . . .' She waved her hands in distraction. How on earth was she going to explain to her old friend that her brother was being his usual, devious self?

It had all started at lunch when, after a heavily silent, tense drive from the beach, she and Luke had arrived at the hotel to find Barbara and her new husband sipping cocktails, together with Corrine and a collection of strangers who were even more casually dressed than she was. It soon transpired that Luke had booked the entire restaurant for their lunch party, and their arrival seemed to be the signal for a barrage of champagne corks, which was almost deafening.

Barbara's husband, Edmond Vignaux, had been a surprise. Far from being the classical idea of a Frenchman—tall, dark and devastatingly handsome— Edmond proved to be short, plump and a good many years older than his young wife. However, it didn't take Samantha very long to realise that, although he was obviously very wealthy, he was also very kind, very charming and—the most important fact of all—both he and Barbara were clearly very much in love with each other.

Preoccupied with her own wretchedly confused, miserable state of mind, Samantha couldn't help feeling a deep pang of envy at her friend's happiness. And then, immediately ashamed of such a petty, small-minded reaction to Barbara's joy and contentment, she forced herself to concentrate as Luke introduced her to the other members of the party. She soon discovered that they were mostly architects, designers and craftsmen concerned with Edmond's current project, which was to restore his old family home to its former glory; and she was just deciding that they were an amusing and interesting bunch of characters when a waiter began filling her glass with more champagne. At the same time, Edmond called for silence, and announced that he wished to propose a toast.

It *must* have been the effect of drinking champagne on an empty stomach. Samantha honestly couldn't think of any other good, valid reason why it should have taken so long for the hideous truth to sink into her thick head. Admittedly, Edmond had been talking very fast, and her ability to speak or understand the French language was fairly minimal—nevertheless, his repeated use of the word *rapprochement*, should have given her *some* idea of what he was talking about, surely? However, it wasn't until he had finished speaking, and she was the recipient of many beaming smiles and winks as they were all being issued through into the dining-room, that the mists began to clear from her brain and she realised what was going on. *Edmond had been toasting a supposed reconciliation between herself and Luke!*

Goodness knew, she certainly didn't want to create a scene in public, but on the other hand . . . 'What do you think you're up to?' she demanded, glaring up at Luke as he came over to stand beside her.

'Me . . .?' he said, raising a dark eyebrow in blank surprise. 'I can't think what you're talking about.'

'Oh, yeah?' She gave a harsh laugh. 'I may not have "ze French" too good, buster, but even *I* got the drift of Edmond's little speech just now!'

'Really? How interesting,' he drawled. 'What did he say?'

'As if you didn't know!' she snapped, her cheeks flaming as she tried to control her temper. He thought he'd got her in a corner, didn't he? He was obviously relying on the fact that nice girls didn't make scenes in restaurants—what a rat the man was! Samantha ground her teeth with fury as she caught the devilish glint of laughter in the depths of his blue eyes. The trouble was, he was right! She didn't want to make a scene, and upset Barbara and her new husband. On the other hand...
'There's no way I'm going to let you push me around,' she hissed. 'Let me tell you...'

'No, not right now, Samantha,' he said firmly. 'We can discuss this matter later, but just at the moment...' he gave a low, sardonic laugh as he gestured to a waiter standing behind her chair, 'I think you'll find everyone is waiting for you to sit down.'

'Oh, hell!' she muttered under her breath, casting a nervous smile around the table as she quickly took her seat. 'But you needn't think that I'm going along with any of your nonsense,' she whispered indignantly a few moments later. 'As far as I'm concerned, you know exactly what you can do with your so-called *rapprochement*!' Her anger increased as he merely greeted her words with a mocking, sardonic laugh before turning to talk to a dark-haired girl with an amazing bust, who was sitting on his other side.

There were enthusiastic murmurs as one delicious course followed another, but the food seemed to turn to cardboard and ashes in her mouth as Samantha tried to think what on earth she was going to do. As much as she would have liked to have buried her sorrows in alcohol, she wasn't able to drink any of the expensive claret which seemed to be circulating around the table at the speed of light. Not only would it be a dangerously stupid thing to do, in view of her intended flight to Antigua later on that afternoon; but in any dealings with her ex-husband, it clearly behoved her to try and keep as clear a head as possible!

In fact, the only faintly amusing aspect of the long, seemingly endless meal was the sight of Corrine's rigid, angry figure. The other girl had clearly been harbouring fond hopes of a rosy future with Luke, and appeared to have completely lost her cool composure following Edmond's announcement; rapidly tipping glasses of wine down her throat as she glared across the table at her employer.

If only she knew the truth, Samantha had thought glumly, trying to work out the geometric variations of what seemed to be a complicated triangular relationship. However, she had been forced to abandon the attempt as the lunch had drawn to a close. And now, as she paced restlessly about the room, she realised that she had absolutely no idea about the depths of Luke's true feelings with regard to his lovely female architect . . . or his wife, for that matter.

'Hey—calm down!' Barbara said with a laugh as she viewed her friend's nervous, agitated figure.

'I can't. I . . .' Samantha waved her hands distractedly in the air. 'I mean . . .' She sighed deeply and turned to face the other girl. 'I—I don't know what Luke has told you. But whatever he's said . . . well, it just isn't true, I'm afraid.'

Barbara stared at her. 'What do you mean? What isn't true?'

'Well . . . you must see that I can't . . . I mean, I really shouldn't be discussing my marriage with you.'

'Why ever not?'

'Because Luke's your brother, and I know you love him very much—that's why not!'

'Sure, I love him, but I'm not blind to his faults, you know,' Barbara grinned. 'So, shoot—what's the problem?'

Samantha hesitated a moment, and then gave a heavy sigh. 'I don't know what sort of game Luke thinks he's playing, but I've got to tell you that there's *no way* I'm going back with him to the States.' She sank down on to a fragile gilt chair and leaned back, staring up at the ceiling. 'And there's absolutely no truth in our so-called reconciliation.'

'Do you mean...?'

'I'll tell you exactly what I mean,' Samantha said firmly. 'I mean, no—I am not going to resume my marriage to your brother, and yes—I definitely want a divorce.'

'I don't believe it!'

Samantha gave an impatient groan. 'Maybe, if I keep on saying the words—*very loudly*—someone will actually hear and believe what I say!'

'Well, it certainly won't be me!' Barbara retorted. 'I've seen the way you two look and act towards each other...'

'Oh, yes?' Samantha's bitter laugh echoed around the room. 'Mostly with rage and fury!'

'Who are you kidding? It's as plain as the freckles on my nose that not only are you and Luke crazy about one another—but you both also just *love* a good, old-fashioned row!'

'We—what...?'

Barbara grinned at the blank astonishment on her friend's face. 'Watching the way you two squared up to one another before lunch—I tell you, I nearly died laughing! It's as clear as daylight that you both get a huge kick out of bawling and squabbling with each other.'

'*You're joking!*'

'It's true!' Barbara insisted. 'Just think for a moment. How many people—other than you and I—ever *really* stand up to my brother? And that's not all, is it? You and Luke have also got another great plus going for you both, haven't you?'

'I don't know what you're talking about,' Samantha muttered, rising from the chair and going over to look out of the window.

The other girl gave an impatient sigh. 'Oh, come on, kiddo! This is your old pal—remember? Why don't we both admit, just between the two of us, that you and Luke always did have a great sexual relationship, huh?'

'*For heaven's sake!*'

'Well...?'

A deep tide of crimson swept over Samantha's face. 'This...this really isn't the sort of thing that...I mean, I can't possibly discuss our private...our intimate life together. And *certainly not* with my husband's sister!' she added crossly.

'I don't see why not. I knew you before you knew Luke—besides which, it's as clear as daylight that you two are mad about each other. And with so much going for you both, I reckon you'd be plum crazy to go ahead with your plans for a divorce. Yes, I know...' Barbara added as Samantha opened her mouth to protest. 'I know that I ought to mind my own business and not interfere, but in a way it *is* my business. If you chuck Luke back into the pond, he's bound to be quickly hooked by someone like Corrine What's-her-name. I mean—how would you like to have a cold, wet fish like her for a sister-in-law, huh?'

'Not much,' Samantha agreed tersely, desperately trying to ignore the tide of green jealousy sweeping through her veins. 'However, Luke's future plans are a matter of supreme indifference as far as I'm concerned,' she added defiantly, before walking over to a chair and picking up her tote bag.

'Oh, yeah...?'

'Yes, well...' she said hastily, ignoring Barbara's sceptical reaction to her words as she turned towards the door. On arriving back here from the restaurant, the last thing she'd felt like had been a tour of the house. But Barbara had been so keen to show her everything that Samantha had forced herself to go through the motions. However, it was definitely time she left, especially since she hadn't liked the colour of the sky when she'd looked outside the window just now.

'I'm sorry to have to cut and run,' she told Barbara. 'I've got to fly to Antigua to see my aunt, and from the look of those dark clouds out there, the sooner I take off, the better.'

Barbara gave a heavy sigh. 'I know my brother has been a complete idiot, but I do wish you'd try and have another go at your marriage, Sam. You're both older and a lot more sensible nowadays; and Luke's told me that he realises it was mostly his fault that it all went wrong.'

'That's...well, that's generous of him,' Samantha said slowly. 'But—no, I can't. I truly am sorry,' she added quietly. 'I wish that it was possible for Luke and myself to get together and live happily ever after, but it just wouldn't work I'm afraid.'

'Well, I'm sorry, too,' Barbara said as they left the room and moved slowly down the corridor towards the large, main hall. 'Not just for my brother's sake, but also because I sure hate to see your aunt winning this round of the game—just as she's won all the others.'

'What?' Samantha turned to stare at her friend. 'What on earth are you talking about?'

'I'm talking about the fact that Luke was so worried and upset when you ran away, that he accepted your Aunt Emily's advice as some sort of gospel truth,' Barbara said grimly. 'All right...' she held up her hand as Samantha began to protest, 'I'm not going to pretend that Luke is—or was—some kind of plaster saint. When you and he were first married, he clearly hadn't any idea how to cope with a young girl—and it's obvious that he was far too possessive. Instead of criticising you, he should have helped you to grow up—assisted you to stand on your own two feet. And I'll freely admit that both my mother and myself have given him hell over the last years for having been so stupid—OK?'

'But...but what's my Aunt Emily got to do with any of this?'

'When you ran away, and landed up with her on that little island, she told Luke that you needed to be left alone for a bit; that you needed time to grow up. And no one—let alone Luke—is disputing the fact that she was right. But that was four years ago, Sam, and although Luke has done everything he can think of, he can't seem to get her to let go.'

Samantha gave a shrill laugh. 'Oh, come on—I've never heard such nonsense! I can promise you that from the moment I left New York, right up to a few days ago, I haven't seen or heard a damn thing from your brother. And why you should be trying to make my aunt into some sort of villain...'

'I'm not,' Barbara assured her quickly. 'Luke's going to kill me for telling you all this, since he's expressly forbidden me to say anything. He's convinced that any criticism of your Aunt Emily will send you rushing immediately, and blindly, to her defence, and is therefore likely to be counter-productive.' Barbara shrugged. 'I happen to think that Luke's far too cautious. In fact, for someone who's supposed to be such a tough businessman, I reckon he's been thoroughly inept and made a complete mess of the whole affair. But I guess that's understandable under the circumstances.'

'What circumstances?' Samantha cried impatiently. 'I haven't a clue what you're talking about.'

'Well...my dear brother is probably an idiot, but it seems he was afraid that if he didn't proceed cautiously, step by step, he'd never get you back.'

'What nonsense!'

'Oh, I agree, *absolutely*!' Barbara grinned. 'We both knew that he should have arrived on the island like an avenging fury, and swept you off your feet with a long, hot session of madly passionate lovemaking. But, there you go—that just shows how stupid some men can be, doesn't it?'

Samantha was ashamed to find herself weakly joining in her friend's rueful laughter. 'Seriously, Barbara, it's all too stupid...'

'Once again—I agree. Luke was stupid, but unfortunately he *did* listen to your aunt, and since he realised that the breakdown of your marriage was mainly his fault, he took her advice and left you strictly alone for the first two years. And when, after that, he tried to contact you, your Aunt Emily always somehow managed to put a spanner in the works. Luke is damn sure that you've never received any of his letters...'

'What letters?'

'There you are—it looks as if he's telling the truth, doesn't it?' Barbara said as she led the way through the hall towards the front door. 'Luke also found that all his phone calls were blocked—although that could just be the normal Caribbean phone service!' She grinned wryly at Samantha. 'Anyway, he got more and more impatient, and when Emily eventually gave in and said he could come and see you, he arrived to find that you were apparently away for a month on a buying trip in Europe. Of course, she was willing to take Luke's money for her crummy old hotel, but I understand that you wouldn't let her accept it, right? And every time he tried to contact you, personally, your dear old aunt made quite sure that you were not available.'

'But I can't believe it! Why—why would she do such a thing? I—I don't understand...'

Her words were interrupted by a sudden influx of people rushing into the hall, chattering and shouting to each other at the top of their voices.

'What's going on?' Samantha asked as Edmond came over to have a quick word with his wife.

'Well, I'm not entirely sure,' Barbara muttered, trying to concentrate as her husband continued to speak in rapid French. 'I gather that there's been an announcement on the radio...something about *un ouragan*, Edmond says, but the others seem to be talking about some sort of a cyclone...'

'Oh, my God—it must be Hurricane Hannah!' Samantha exclaimed. 'Is it going to hit this island?'

'*Non* ... not zis island. *Non St Barthélemy, ca ne peut pas arriver ici,*' Edmond said firmly.

'If I understood the radio announcement correctly, we're outside the main path of the hurricane—which seems to be travelling west,' Luke said as he came up to join them. 'It's being tracked by radar and satellite, and apparently the best guess at the moment is that it's likely to miss Guadeloupe and Antigua. Hey...! Where are you going?' he demanded as Samantha dragged open the front door and ran outside.

'Just look at that sky!' she cried, pointing up at the black clouds which were beginning to obliterate the sun. 'I've got to borrow your car, Barbara. I'll leave it at the airport,' she shouted, running fast across the gravel forecourt, before a hand grasped her arm and she was spun around to face her husband.

'What do you think you're doing? You *can't* be so insane as to think of flying to Antigua—not through those clouds,' he roared furiously. 'I know you're worried about your aunt, but...'

'Don't be stupid,' she snapped. 'It's not my aunt I'm chiefly worried about. St Pauls doesn't seem to be in any danger at the moment, but hurricanes are notoriously unpredictable. I must get back to the island—and the hotel full of guests for whom I'm totally responsible—as soon as possible!'

CHAPTER EIGHT

'GOLF Bravo Alpha Lima Tango to St Martin tower. Over.'

'Go ahead, Alpha Lima Tango. Over.'

Samantha pushed the transmit button on the handset. 'Lima Tango. Request clearance for take-off: St Barthélemy to St Pauls via Antigua. Over.'

There was no reply, the empty crackling sound from the receiver, fixed to a panel above her head in the cockpit, barely audible over the roar of the Cessna's engines as Samantha taxied the aeroplane over the rough, bumpy grass towards the end of the runway. It was hot and muggy within the confined space of the aeroplane, and she quickly wiped the sweat from her brow as she once again requested permission to take off.

'Please wait, Lima Tango. Over.'

Oh, no! It looked as if, once again, the over-worked Aircraft Control on the nearby island of St Martin were being hard pressed to cope with the ever-increasing air traffic. She'd once sat out here, on the runway, for well over half an hour while she'd waited for clearance. But she couldn't afford to waste that amount of time today— not when it was imperative that she returned to St Pauls as soon as possible. She'd just have to take off, and contact the control tower again when she was airborne.

Pausing for a final check of her instruments, she took a deep breath and pushed the throttle hard forward. The aircraft quickly gathered speed and momentum, hurtling forward towards the mountain at the end of the runway. Just when it seemed as if the plane was destined

150

to crash into the rocky, grass-and tree-covered obstruction ahead, she pulled hard back on the joystick
and the aeroplane rose in the air, sailing over the
mountain and up into the darkening sky.

'Lima Tango calling St Martin tower. Am now airborne. Request height clearance for St Pauls via Antigua.
Over.'

There was a crackle of static from the receiver.
*'Weather conditions deteriorating, Lima Tango. Suggest
you return to base. Over.'*

'Cannot return to base. Am setting course for Antigua.
Request clearance for fifteen hundred feet. Over.'

There was another long pause, the only noise in the
cabin being the crackle of static from the receiver, and
the steady drone of the plane's engines.

'Return to base, Lima Tango.' The voice on the intercom sounded agitated. *'Hurricane warning. Winds
Force Twelve. You must return to base immediately!'*

Samantha grimaced, casting a quick sideways glance
at the man sitting silent and immobile beside her. She
had warned Luke that this flight wasn't going to be a
joyride, but it was beginning to look as if she might have
severely underestimated the difficulties in trying to get
back to St Pauls. Of course, she should never have taken
off without clearance; and it seemed as if, in assuming
that the hold-up in St Martin was just a temporary, technical gremlin in the works, she had made a very bad
mistake.

'It sounds as if you've got problems,' Luke said
quietly.

'Hmm . . .' she murmured, preoccupied in doing complicated sums in her head. Taking into account her flight
speed, and the amount of fuel she had on board, to
return to St Barts and try to land in the storm which
must have reached it by now was to invite almost as much

trouble as pressing on to St Pauls. It was a gamble either way—and when she thought about the hotel, full of guests for whom she was responsible, it didn't seem as if she had a choice. Still, at least Luke wasn't likely to add to her problems. She knew from the past that, once Luke made up his mind to a course of action, he wasn't the type to start crying over spilt milk—or to say 'I told you so'—however much he might be justified in doing so. In fact, she realised with some surprise as she brushed the damp curls from her brow, she really couldn't think of anyone else she'd rather have as a companion on what was clearly going to be a difficult, if not downright dangerous flight.

Not that she'd thought so on the mad dash from Edmond and Barbara's house at Pointe Milou to the airport! She'd been furious when Luke had jumped into the mini-moke as she was driving away, and thoroughly fed up with his non-stop harangue on her impetuosity, her refusal to face the hard facts of life, and the folly of even thinking about returning to St Pauls and the Hamilton Plantation Hotel.

'It's a ridiculous idea,' he told her angrily, for the umpteenth time, as she drove quickly past the sandy beach which edged the Baie de St Jean.

'Oh—*shut up!*' she snarled, responding to Luke's words by slamming her foot hard down on the accelerator.

Luke shuddered and closed his eyes for a moment as the mini-moke roared around a sharp left-hand bend on what appeared to be only two wheels. On opening them again, he clearly wished he hadn't, wincing as his vision filled with the depressing sight of ornately carved monuments and large, white crosses as the vehicle sped past a cemetery, which was situated across the road from the fenced-off area of St Jean airport.

'This is a totally hare-brained scheme...rash and reckless action which is likely to...'

Samantha swept into the car park reserved for airport personnel and pilots, bringing the vehicle to a screeching halt, before wrenching her door open and running around to the rear of the car. 'Why don't you get lost? I've had nothing but *nag-nag* and *yak-yak* from you for the last ten minutes,' she cried, angrily kicking off her shoes as she leaned inside the back of the car for her flying suit. 'Who asked you to come along, anyway?'

'There are times when I could cheerfully wring your neck—and this is *definitely* one of them!' he grated furiously. 'What the hell do you hope to achieve by flying back to St Pauls? That's if you manage to reach the island—which seems very unlikely, if those black thunder clouds are anything to go by,' he added grimly, glancing up at the darkening sky.

'Thanks for the vote of confidence!'

Luke gave a heavy sigh, striving to control his anger and impatience. 'I have a considerable amount of confidence in your flying ability, Samantha. But that's not the point, is it?' he pressed urgently as he watched her zip up her suit. 'Heaven knows, I'm no pilot—but even I can see that in trying to take off in the coming storm, you're taking a considerable risk.'

'For goodness' sake—calm down! I'm going to be flying in the opposite direction to those clouds up there, so that thunderstorm isn't going to bother me. Besides, I really *must* try and get back to St Pauls.'

'That's nonsense!'

'No, it's not,' she insisted, slipping on her sneakers and reaching behind his tall figure to pull her tote bag out of the car. 'Someone has to look after all the guests in the hotel—and then there's the staff as well, don't forget. I can't just abandon them, can I?'

'And if Hurricane Hannah should change course?' he demanded harshly. 'What then?'

She shrugged. 'OK, I'll admit there is a slim chance that it might change course, but that's even more reason for me to try and get back to the hotel. If the worst comes to the worst, by taking off now I should be back on the island long before the hurricane arrives, which will give me plenty of time to get everyone down into the hotel cellars, where they'll be quite safe. So, simmer down—OK?' she added as she began walking swiftly towards a gate in the fence which surrounded the airfield.

'No—of course it's not "OK"...!' he ground out through clenched teeth. 'Come back here, at once!'

'I'm perfectly able to look after myself—and I'm not going to stand around here arguing with you,' she called out. 'Give my love to Barbara. 'Bye.'

Closing the gate behind her, Samantha glanced down at her wristwatch and then ran as quickly as she could across the grass towards the Cessna, which was parked beside the end of the runway near the sea. Leaping up on to the wing of the aeroplane, she was just pulling open the door when she staggered and almost fell as she felt a firm hand grip her ankle.

'Oh, no!' she groaned, turning to stare down at Luke's hard, implacable face. 'I won't let you...you're not going to stop me...!' she panted, still breathless from her dash across the airfield.

Luke gave a harsh bark of laughter. 'I think you've already made that fact quite clear,' he said, pulling himself up on to the wing beside her.

'What the hell do you think you're doing?'

'There's a well-known expression—"If you can't beat 'em...join 'em",' he retorted, firmly moving her to one side so that he could enter the aircraft. 'Hurry up, we obviously haven't much time,' he added crisply, sitting himself down in the front passenger seat.

'My God—you've got a damn nerve!' she grated, peering into the cockpit and glowering angrily at his long-legged figure.

It didn't, however, take more than a few seconds' thought for her to realise that there wasn't a thing she could do about the situation. Luke was right: there was no time to shilly-shally around; no time to argue about Who was going Where—and How. Glancing up at the black clouds which were getting nearer every moment, Samantha realised that she had only a very little time in which to get the aeroplane off the runway.

'Oh—all right,' she grumbled. 'If you're determined to come with me, then I suppose I'm lumbered with you. But I want you to listen hard—and listen real good,' she said, quickly settling into the pilot's seat and doing up her seat-belt. 'The first thing I'd better tell you is that—as you've so graphically pointed out already—the weather isn't too good. It's likely to be a bumpy ride, and so if you want to jump out, now is the time to do so.'

As Luke gave a silent shrug of his shoulders, her point about the weather was emphasised by the increasingly noisy twanging of the wires attached to the aeroplane. Caught by the rising wind, they beat a continuous, rapid tattoo against the outside of the fuselage.

'Secondly, I'm the pilot, right?' she continued, her hands moving smoothly and confidently over the controls in front of her. 'Now, you can say and do what you like when you're in the offices of Brandon-Phillips International, in New York or wherever. But here and now, in this aeroplane, *I'm* in charge and *I* call the shots. OK?'

'Wow—the Red Baron flies again!' he murmured sardonically under his breath.

'*What* did you say?' she demanded angrily.

Luke raised his dark eyebrows in cool mockery. 'Me...?' he queried blandly. 'After that little speech of yours, I certainly wouldn't dream of saying anything.'

'That's a very sensible decision!' she told him grimly. 'Because I don't want to have any advice, discussions, instructions or any other nonsense from you while I'm flying this plane. And the last thing I need is to have you panicking, or screaming blue murder during the flight, like that pathetic girlfriend of yours.'

Other than a tightening of his lips at the mention of his relationship with Corrine, Luke remained silent, continuing to regard her with a calm, impassive expression on his face, which she found distinctively unnerving.

'OK. Now, for your information, I'd better explain that there's no aircraft control in St Barts. All air traffic is controlled from the large nearby island of St Martin...' She paused as the left-hand engine caught and fired, and she leant forward to check the oil pressure and the alternator. 'Right, that's the port engine started, now for the starboard one,' she muttered, pulling the throttle half-open and turning the master switch as she began going through the whole, detailed sequence once again.

'As you've already pointed out, *ad nauseam*,' she continued, 'this flight isn't exactly going to be a breeze or a joyride. Are you sure that you don't want to high-tail it out of here right now?'

'No—I'm not at all sure!' he had drawled smoothly, settling back in his seat and calmly folding his arms across his chest. 'But since you seem quite determined to commit hara-kiri...' he turned his head to give her a sardonic grin, 'then I guess that I don't have any option but to join you, hmm?'

And she certainly had to hand it to Luke, Samantha thought, as she now struggled to hold the plane steady against the increasingly strong guests of wind. As instructed, her husband had barely opened his mouth or moved an inch since their take-off. In fact, other than noticing that his face seemed somewhat paler than normal, as far as she could see, Luke appeared to be totally relaxed and seemingly without a care in the world.

Wishing that she was capable of being equally laid-back, Samantha took a deep breath to calm her rising apprehension as she once again picked up the transmitter, and requested flight clearance for two thousand feet.

'Negative, Lima Tango, we can give you no clearance—repeat, negative clearance. Return to base. Over.'

'Lima Tango—now heading zero-nine-zero. Over,' she persisted.

It quickly became clear that the rapidly deteriorating weather was causing problems, and not just to her own light aircraft. As black, dense clouds completely enveloped the Cessna, the disembodied voice of the air-traffic controller was interrupted by sharp whistles and crackling, so that she was barely able to hear the few words that spelt out the stark conditions into which she was flying.

'...danger...Lima Tango...hurricane...American Airlines Boeing and three other unidentified aircraft...your vicinity. Urgent...extreme danger...' And then both the voice and the noisy atmospherics died completely away, leaving the aeroplane totally silent save for the background hum of the engines.

Samantha hardly had time to worry about her predicament. Continuing to try and make contact with air-traffic control, she quickly abandoned the attempt as a sudden, huge gust of wind and rain hit the aircraft. Desperately fighting to keep the plane steady against the driving force of the storm, she was almost blinded as a rapid streak of lightning flashed across the nose of the aeroplane. At that precise moment, the light in the cockpit went out, and in total darkness the aircraft dropped down hundreds of feet, like a heavy stone thrown into a deep well.

Knowing that the altimeter must be spinning backwards at the rate of knots—and that there was nothing she could do about it—Samantha gritted her teeth and tried to stop herself trembling as she struggled to regain control of the aeroplane. Eventually managing to bring the Cessna up on to an even keel, she was pathetically grateful when the light flickered on again. It wasn't just the fact that she was now able to see the various dials and gauges that was so important. While the aircraft continued to be roughly buffeted, and thrown around the sky by the electrical storm raging outside, having some illumination inside the cabin somehow made the Stygian darkness outside seem less frightening. Not that she was able to fool herself. It was going to take some sort of miracle if she, and Luke, were to survive the hazards which lay ahead.

'I . . . I guess I've been a damn fool,' she said, trying to control the wobble in her voice as she turned to give Luke a quick, nervous glance.

'There's no point in crying over spilt milk, sweetheart.'

Luke sounded so calm and confident that she realised he didn't appreciate just what dangerous straits they were in. For one, desperate moment she felt an overwhelming longing to put her head on his shoulder and bawl her eyes out. But she couldn't possibly do that—not when she'd gone to such great lengths to impress upon him that she was such a hard, tough cookie.

'Samantha...?'

She took a deep breath to try and steady her nerves. 'Yes, well...I'd better be frank and confess that things don't look too good.'

That must be one of the understatements of the year! she added grimly to herself. And it wasn't just the plane that looked as if it might be in trouble. The muscles in her arms were aching, and she was beginning to feel desperately tired, both from the mental stress of the situation, and the physical energy required to hold the aircraft steady against the force of the wind.

'In fact, Luke, if you think it might work— maybe...er...maybe this is the time to start saying a few prayers...?' she muttered huskily, swallowing hard against a rising tide of panic.

'That bad, huh?'

'Mm-hm.'

She was surprised, both by the comforting warmth of Luke's hand as he grasped her trembling knee, and the dry amusement in his voice as he assured her, 'As they say: "the opera's never over till the fat lady sings"...! So, relax, sweetheart. We're going to beat this little problem—no sweat!'

'Luke Brandon's personal guarantee?' she asked, a slight catch in her voice as she gave him a shaky, wobbly smile.

'Absolutely!'

'Oh, Luke...!' She bit her lip and then took a deep breath. 'I think I'd better tell you...' She paused as another flash of lightning zigzagged across the sky, and she fought to control the plane as it lurched downwards once more. 'It isn't just the storm. I—I don't know if you followed what the man was saying over the intercom, but somewhere out there...' She nodded towards the black clouds surrounding the aircraft. 'Well, it seems that there are four other aeroplanes...'

'Four? In that mess?'

She nodded. 'A large passenger jet and three small aircraft.'

'Oh-oh. That doesn't sound too good.'

'It isn't. Because, other than the jet, none of them is likely to have any radar on board. Which means that there's a very strong chance that at least one of us is going to run into another plane. And if that happens...'

'We'll be sitting on a cloud, harp in hand and learning how to fly with *real* wings?'

'Yes—I'm afraid so,' she agreed in a small, tearful voice.

'OK, so that's the bad news,' Luke said, his voice sounding calm and confident, although as she glanced at his face she saw a pulse beating rapidly in his jaw, and there were beads of sweat on his forehead. 'Is there any good news?'

She shook her head. 'Unfortunately, no—not really. I...I'm flying as fast as this aircraft will travel—the sort of equivalent of putting my foot hard down on a car's accelerator,' she explained. 'What I'm hoping is that if we can succeed in avoiding all the other planes which are out there in the clouds somewhere, we may manage to outfly the storm. But I've only a rough idea of where we are at the moment, and it ... it's such a slim hope...' Her voice died away and she gave a helpless shrug of her shoulders.

Her eyes felt gritty and her limbs trembled under the strain as she stared numbly at the compass. Had she chosen the right heading? It was a total gamble and the stakes were impossibly high. A wave of tiredness seemed to wash through her body, along with a stupefying feeling of futility. There was no way of knowing the height and speed of the other aircraft, and even if she could avoid them, she couldn't fly into any airport without radio contact—which was also a vital necessity if she was to attempt landing in this murky darkness. All she could do was to keep flying, and hope to God that she didn't run out of fuel, because if so...

The long silence was broken by the sound of Luke clearing his throat. 'I guess we must have reached the point in the disaster movie where someone runs amok, the other passengers start singing "My country, 'tis of thee", and the little old lady of ninety—who's never flown before in her life—takes over the controls of the plane!'

'Thanks for those few words of comfort!' Samantha was surprised to find herself giving him a weak, shaky grin, her tense body relaxing slightly as she continued to peer through the thick, black cloud outside the cockpit.

'That's better,' he said, reaching over to give her hand a brief squeeze. 'You're doing fine, sweetheart. I have every confidence that you're going to get us out of this mess—so try and keep as cool and as calm as you can, OK?'

'You...you really believe we're going to make it?'

'I most certainly do,' he said firmly. 'Fear is a far more dangerous enemy than a few small planes out there in that vast sky,' he added, his strong personality continuing to support and encourage her faltering belief in their survival as the minutes ticked slowly by.

'...Besides which,' he concluded with a laugh. 'There's no way I'm going to Kingdom Come with so many loose ends lying around. And that's that!'

'Luke Brandon is now dictating terms to the Almighty?' she asked with a wobbly smile.

He grinned. 'Why not? I'm sure that whoever's up there will perfectly understand that I need some more time down here. After all, quite apart from anything else, I need time in which to try and convince you of a few, very important facts.'

'Such as...?'

'Such as the fact that I completely lost my heart to you, the very first time I laid eyes on you—and that there has *never* been anyone else for me, from that day to this. And the fact that I was a damn fool not to realise the trouble Adele was causing to our marriage.'

'You mean...'

'She was lying,' he said firmly. 'God knows why— because I most certainly never made love to her. She was a very efficient assistant—and that's all she was. Besides, Adele was the sort of girl who wouldn't go to bed with a man, not unless there was a very clear wedding ring in view.'

'And Corrine...?' she muttered, staring at the instrument panel in front of her. The force of the wind seemed to have abated somewhat, and it was proving easier to keep the plane on an even keel. 'What about your relationship with Corrine?'

Luke sighed. 'You're such a fool, sweetheart! Is it likely, when I came to St Pauls for the sole purpose of trying to get you to come back to me, that I'd be stupid enough to bring a girlfriend along to keep me company?' He gave a harsh, sardonic bark of laughter. 'I do think that you might have given me credit for having *some* intelligence.'

'Yes...well...' Samantha's cheeks flushed as she stared out of the cockpit at the enveloping darkness. 'But I thought...I thought you were there to buy the hotel,' she added lamely.

'That was just an excuse for being on the island. There wasn't anything that couldn't be handled by one of my staff,' he said dismissively. 'And that's all Corrine was— a good architect whom I employed to do a job of work. End of story. I promise you that there has been no other woman in my life since you left,' he added, his voice heavy with sincerity.

'Not one? In four years?' she gave an incredulous laugh. 'Now it's your turn to give me credit for having some intelligence!'

'OK, OK...' he grinned, a slight flush reddening his cheeks. 'I'll admit that when you walked out on me, I was so damn mad with both you and the world in general that I...' He sighed and shrugged his broad shoulders. 'However, I very soon found out that I didn't want anyone else. I wanted you. But I wanted you to trust me; to *know* in your heart of hearts that I'm not the sort of guy who two-times his wife; to realise that I meant every single word of the marriage vows we made together. Was that too much to ask?'

'Well, I...'

'I guess it was,' he continued. 'I can now see that trust is something that needs time to flourish; time in which two people can really get to know one another. And I was always far too busy and preoccupied with work, wasn't I?' Luke gave a heavy sigh, brushing his fingers roughly through his dark hair. 'I was a damn fool, and it's largely my fault that our marriage didn't work out. It's taken me a long time—and, God knows, I sure hate to admit defeat!—but I guess I've finally come to accept the fact that you really do want a divorce.'

'Oh, Luke! I've been so...so...' There seemed to be a large lump in her throat and she had difficulty in

swallowing. How could she possibly ever begin to explain that it had taken until now for her to realise—when
it was far, far too late—that not only did she love this
hard, tough man with all her heart, but that all the
stresses and strains of the past now seemed totally un-
important? The relationship between them, once so full
of misery and tension, was now one based on a far more
equal, mature footing. Barbara had been right. Odd as
it might seem—and it certainly had taken her a long time
to discover the truth—she and Luke really *did* enjoy arguing with each other, both of them even going as far
as to relish a good fight! And now, because of her own
blind stupidity, she had thrown away all her chances of
future happiness.

'I—I don't know what to say...' she added in a
strangled voice, bitterly ashamed of the fact that there
was nothing she could do to prevent her eyes from filling
with hopeless tears.

'Hey—there's no need to cry, sweetheart,' he murmured tenderly, leaning across to gently wipe her eyes
with his handkerchief.

'You...you don't understand,' she sniffed, trying to
think how to explain that the last thing she now wanted
was a divorce—especially when, only a few hours ago,
she had so firmly declared that she did.

'Sure I do. There are a lot of people who really care
about each other—but, for one reason or another, they
just can't seem to live together. I guess we fall into that
category, hmm? And it's because I love you, and want
you to be happy, that I promise—if we manage to survive
this mess!—that I'll fix up a quiet divorce. OK?'

'But you can't do that!' she wailed. 'Not when I've
only just realised...'

'*My God—you've done it!*'

Luke's jubilant shout resounded around the interior of the cockpit as the small aircraft suddenly broke through the black clouds into the normal, hazy sunshine of a Caribbean afternoon. The contrast between the smothering, dark mass of dense vapour which had enveloped them for so long, and the brilliant azure-blue sky in which they were now flying, was so extraordinarily dramatic that it was a second or two before Samantha could come to terms with their miraculous deliverance.

'*So I have!*' she exclaimed at last, and then they were both overcome with hysterical laughter as they revelled in the euphoric relief of having escaped from dire peril—and the sheer, overwhelming joy of being alive.

Luke pointed towards an island ahead. 'Is that St Pauls?'

'Yup—it looks like we're home and dry,' she grinned, her smile slowly giving way to consternation as they drew nearer to the small airstrip. 'I don't understand,' she muttered, banking the plane so that she could stare down. 'It looks as if...'

'Is that an aeroplane?' he asked, peering down at what seemed to be various bits and pieces of a broken toy lying on the grass runway.

'Oh, lord—we must be too late! I—I don't understand, but it looks as if the hurricane must have somehow struck the island before we got here!' she cried. 'What on earth am I going to do? I can't land there—not without hitting some of that debris.'

He put a warning hand on her shoulder. 'Calm down, and take a deep breath, OK? We've come this far—so the rest *has* to be a piece of cake! Cool down...that's right. Good girl!' he added as she began to relax her tense, strained body. 'Now, let's begin to start thinking

straight again, hmm? Is there anywhere else you can land
on the island?'

'Well...' She frowned and tried to concentrate on the
problem. She was feeling so tired that it seemed an age
before she managed to cudgel her weary brain into
finding a solution to the problem. 'The beach in front
of the hotel is too short, but maybe...yes, there is another
stretch just around the corner of the bay. I'm not
sure...but it might be possible to land there.'

'It doesn't look as if we've any choice—unless you
think you can make it to Antigua?'

Samantha shook her head wearily. 'No, I haven't
enough fuel, and if the storm has caused that amount
of damage to the plane on the airstrip...well, I must
try and get back to the hotel.'

'OK—let's go for it!'

Her hands were damp with sweat, slipping on the
joystick as she turned and flew low over the sea towards
the proposed site. The fuel gauges looked pretty well
empty, which would reduce the risk of fire, she thought,
desperately trying to force herself into doing the vital
checks before attempting a landing.

'You'd better strap yourself in as tightly as you can,'
she warned Luke, circling widely over the narrow strip
of beach as she debated with herself the best approach
for a landing.

'Good luck, sweetheart,' he muttered.

'I'm going to need it,' she said, checking the airspeed
indicator and making a wide, banking turn to line up
the nose of the Cessna on the unusual airstrip. 'Well...'
she added with a shaky laugh, 'here goes nothing!'

Putting on full flaps, she trimmed the plane as carefully as she could, the controls feeling mushy beneath
her hands as the aircraft lost airspeed. The beach looked

so short, so narrow... She set her teeth and concentrated as never before in her life. She was only going to get one go at this landing—and she was going to have to get it right.

Slowly gliding down, she closed the throttle completely as the wheels grazed the sand at the end of the beach. Everything seemed to be going well, until there was a sickening crunch, the airframe shuddering as the undercarriage struck a rock and the fuselage collapsed on to the sand, sliding with a horrifically frightening tearing sound towards the far end of the beach.

Samantha fought with the controls, wrestling frantically as she tried to keep the aircraft pointing in a straight line. Oh, God! She'd misjudged the speed and landed too fast. She'd never be able to stop... When it was almost too late, she suddenly saw another pile of rocks ahead. In desperation, and using her last, dwindling reserves of strength, she swung the rudder hard over, the fuselage of the Cessna swerving violently around with a loud, rasping sound like that of sandpaper on glass. And then, as if in slow motion, it seemed as if her side of the aircraft was caving in, and she barely registered the heavy blow to her head.

Bracing himself for the crash, Luke watched helplessly as the aeroplane spun sharply to the left and then— miraculously!—came to a shuddering, juddering halt beside some tall, jagged rocks, its nose buried deep in a sandbank.

'That's my girl!' he laughed with relief, punching the release buckle on his harness before turning to Samantha. 'I swear I never thought that we'd... *Oh, no...!*' he cried, his eyes widening in horror as he saw the steady flow of blood trickling down the pale, ashen cheeks of the limp figure lying unconscious in the seat beside him.

* * *

Samantha surfaced from the depths of a dark, swirling mist, her eyelids fluttering as she gazed blindly up at Luke's face, only inches away from her own. Where was she? And why... why did she feel so weightless, and yet have this peculiar feeling that she was somehow still travelling...? Gradually, her dazed confusion gave way to a deep, pounding headache and the dim, foggy realisation that she was being carried in her husband's arms as he made his way over rugged sand dunes at the edge of the beach.

'L-Luke...' she whispered, closing her eyes as the pain in her head intensified. 'Where...? The plane...?'

'Hush, darling. Don't worry, everything's going to be all right,' he murmured, clutching her firmly to his chest as, without slackening his pace, he lowered his head to press his lips to her brow.

'But I—I must...please...put me down...let me go...' she gasped.

His arms tightened convulsively about her. 'I'm never letting you go again. Never!' he said fiercely, the breath rasping in his throat as he struggled over the shifting sand towards a plantation of palm trees. 'Just hang on in there, sweetheart. It won't be long now,' he added, but she didn't hear him as their jolting progress proved too painful for her aching head to cope with, a low moan breaking from her lips as she lapsed back into the dark mists once more.

CHAPTER NINE

SAMANTHA finally returned to full consciousness, slowly becoming aware of a confused background noise of excited conversation and a heavy, rumbling sound as if some heavy object was being dragged across a wooden floor. She felt a cold cloth being placed on her forehead, and, as she opened her eyes, the worried face of Betty Finberg swam before her vision.

'What's happened...? Ouch!' Samantha winced with pain as she turned her head, astonished to find herself lying on a sofa in the middle of the lounge of the Hamilton Plantation Hotel.

'You must be careful, honey. You've had a nasty crack on the head,' Betty said, removing the cloth from Samantha's head, and replacing it with another from a bowl of cold water on the floor beside her. 'Now, just take it easy,' she added as the younger girl struggled to sit up.

'But what about Luke? And the plane? And...and I thought the hurricane had been through here, but...'

'Whoa—relax!' Betty murmured, pressing her back on to the cushions. 'First of all, that husband of yours is just fine. He's out the back getting all the staff organised, but I'm sure he'll be up here to see you just as soon as he can. As for your aunt's aeroplane—Luke tells me that it's a write-off, I'm afraid. But at least you got back here safely, in one piece and in time—that's the main thing, isn't it?' she added soothingly.

Samantha frowned, gritting her teeth against the pounding ache in her head. 'I—well, I don't under-

stand. Why is Luke organising the staff, and what about
the hurricane? The hotel doesn't seem to have been
damaged, and—oh Betty...' she groaned. 'Just now, I'd
sell my soul for a couple of aspirins!'

'Right here.' The older woman carefully helped her to
sit up, and then placed two tablets and a glass of water
in her trembling hands. 'You'll feel better soon,' she
promised.

'Oh, God—I hope so!'

'Sure you will,' Betty said comfortingly, before briefly
narrating the story of the flight from St Barts, as told
to her by Luke, and the final emergency landing on a
beach near the hotel.

'Heavens to Betsy! I nearly *died* when I saw this man
striding up over the lawn—and there you were, lying all
limp and unconscious in his arms!' Betty sighed and
shook her head.

'But what about...'

'...Hurricane Hannah? Well, the fact is that while
we've heard the warning on the radio, we're still waiting
to see if it's going to hit the island. Which is why that
handsome husband of yours is busy getting everyone organised at the moment,' Betty explained. 'All the guests
have been given various jobs to do—why, even my Hector
is busy running around like a two-year-old!'

'I—I'm sure that I saw a plane scattered all over the
runway...and that's why I thought the hurricane had
already hit the island. Or, at least, I—I *think* I saw a
plane...' Samantha paused, closing her eyes for a
moment as she tried to recall all that had happened since
that swift, hurried departure from St Barts. Unfortunately, the sequence of events seemed to be jumbled up
in her mind, and, although she could vividly remember
the terrifying tension of the flight itself, she had little or
no recollection of her crash-landing on the beach.

'Yes, how about that aircraft scattered all over the airport!' Betty exclaimed. 'Lester has just been telling me all about it. It seems some rich college boy, who's staying here on the island, had a mite too much to drink before lunch, and then decided to show off in front of his girlfriend. The silly young fool, who'd had only a few flying lessons, completely misjudged his landing and managed to smash up his daddy's new aeroplane. And would you believe it—that boy walked away from the crash without even a scratch!'

Trying to ignore the sledge-hammer still pounding away in her head, Samantha looked around the hotel lounge. She hadn't been imagining that noise just now. All the heavy furniture had been dragged to the sides of the room and piled up against the walls, heavy ropes being used to tie the smaller pieces together. Even as she watched, she was amazed to see the gardener, Jason, and two other helpers marching into the room carrying planks of wood, which they proceeded to begin nailing up over the windows.

'Hey!' she called out weakly. 'What do you think you're doing?'

'We gotta board up these windows,' Jason replied. 'I done told you that there was a storm coming,' he added, a clearly discernible note of triumphant satisfaction in his voice.

'You can't do that. Stop it, at once!'

'Master Brandon says we is to do as he says,' Jason retorted, barely pausing to answer her as he continued banging nails into the ancient mahogany wall-panelling, which was her aunt's pride and joy.

'Oh, he did, did he?' she grated angrily, swinging her legs off the sofa and struggling to stand up. 'I'm feeling much better,' she said firmly, ignoring Betty's urgent protestations that she ought to stay lying down, as she forced herself to walk—admittedly, somewhat un-steadily—out of the lounge in search of her husband.

It took her some time, but she eventually tracked him down at the far end of the kitchen, where he was super-vising the assembly of what seemed to be endless buckets of water.

'What on earth are you doing here, sweetheart?' he asked, coming over to put an arm around her waist and looking down at her with deep concern. 'Betty assured me that you haven't been seriously hurt, but I'd like you to go back up to the lounge and lie down. There's nothing you can do here for the time being.'

'I want a word with you, Luke,' she said sharply.

'Yes, of course, darling, but I'm busy just at the moment. So, if you'll just go and put your feet up...'

'Now!' she demanded curtly.

Luke studied her carefully for a moment, and then shrugged his shoulders before giving his helpers—a mixture of guests and staff—some more tasks to carry out. 'OK,' he said, leading her away into an empty wine cellar. 'What's the problem?'

'There isn't a problem—or not one that can't be solved, very quickly,' she grated. 'I'm not prepared to have my aunt's hotel ruined—and I'm certainly not going to have nails driven in to her antique panelling! If the guests are fool enough to do what you tell them—well, that's their problem; but I want to know what gives you the right to think you can order the hotel staff around? You have absolutely no authority to do so, and...and I won't have it!'

To her complete surprise—and fury!—he threw back his head and roared with laughter.

'I don't see what's so damn funny,' she grated angrily.

'You're not just funny, sweetheart,' he drawled with sardonic amusement. 'You're absolutely *priceless*!'

'Oh, yes...?' she bristled.

He grinned. 'I really can't think of *any* other woman who, only half an hour after crash-landing an aeroplane which she has flown through a terrifyingly dangerous electrical storm—and incidentally managing to knock herself unconscious—would then pick herself up and start bitching about who does what in this damn hotel!'

'I'm not bitching,' she snapped.

'Oh, yes, you are—and it's going to stop, right now,' he said firmly, all trace of amusement fading rapidly from his face. 'We aren't getting too much information through on the radio link with Antigua, but the best guess seems to be that this island is likely to avoid the main force of Hurricane Hannah. However, it looks as if we *are* going to be hit by the tail end of the storm. If so, we have very little time in hand before it arrives, and I'm not prepared to risk my life, and the lives of others, in long-drawn-out discussions. As from now, I'm the boss around here, and you will do exactly what I tell you to. Right?'

'Absolutely dead wrong!' she stormed, wincing as a flash of pain zigzagged through her head. 'Why should you think that you can order me and the others about?'

'Because I know the basic facts and figures on how best to survive in hurricane conditions, and I'm sure that you have only a hazy idea of how to go about it,' he said grimly. 'You're aunt's precious panelling, for instance, isn't going to be worth a damn when the storm strikes this island—because with winds travelling anything up to seventy miles an hour, much of this hotel isn't likely to remain standing! Boarding up the windows may *just* save it—but I wouldn't bank on that, if I were you.'

Samantha stared up at the man exuding such forceful, masculine authority. As always, despite the tension of the situation and the chaotic state of the hotel surroundings, Luke was looking his usual cool, immaculate

self. Granted, he had somehow found the time to change
into a pair of faded blue jeans, and the stone-washed,
blue cotton shirt stretched across his broad shoulders
had clearly seen better days; but nevertheless, both gar-
ments looked as if they had just come straight from the
laundry.

It was so damned unfair, because she was only too
well aware that she looked a complete and utter mess.
Goodness knew what had happened to her flying suit,
but her slacks and T-shirt were now dusty and stained
with oil and blood. As for her hair...! Not that she really
cared what she looked like, of course, and she knew that
she really shouldn't be thinking about anything so frivolous at such a time as this—but it did somehow put her
at a considerable disadvantage in this confrontation. Besides which... Samantha gave a heavy sigh. It was no
good trying to fool herself—she knew in her heart of
hearts that Luke was right. They were in a desperately
dangerous situation, and it was stupid as well as futile
of her to oppose him without having any good, sensible
grounds for doing so. And the final clincher, if she
needed it, was the realisation that she was feeling far too
tired and weary to put up anything more than a token
resistance.

'Well...?' he demanded curtly.

'OK—we'll do it your way,' she muttered.

Luke looked down at the girl, his hard blue eyes soft-
ening as he saw that she was almost swaying with
exhaustion. 'Come along,' he said, gently leading her
back into the kitchen and sitting her down on a chair.
'Now, I want you to relax,' he added, squatting down
beside her and taking her trembling hands in his, almost
as if he was willing some of his strength into her weary
body. 'There's an awful lot to do, and very little time
to do it in. I've asked that smart girl, Penny, to get some
of the male guests to haul a load of mattresses down

here into the cellar. As you so rightly pointed out, back
in St Barts, when the tail end of the hurricane strikes
this is going to be the only reasonably safe place in which
to shelter. So, my main efforts are going to be concentrated on making it as comfortable as possible. All right?'

She nodded, feeling almost too tired to say anything,
and pathetically grateful to be able to sit down and rest
her trembling legs.

'Now, you of all people should know who's who in
this hotel, right? So, as Lester and I begin herding all
the guests and hotel staff down here, I want you to make
a list of all of their names. I guess that I don't have to
tell you that it's going to be *very* important that we keep
a close check on everyone—and it may be necessary to
run regular roll-calls. All right?'

'Yes, I...' She took a deep breath, staring fixedly down
at the strong brown hands so firmly clasping her own
trembling fingers. 'Of course I'll do all I can to help.
You're quite right...there can only be one person in
charge of all the arrangements, and I...I'm sorry for
being so stupid as to lose my temper just now.'

Luke gave a low laugh of warm, tender amusement.
'Oh, Samantha! Coming from you—that's a really *terrific* apology! Hey, now, don't spoil it...!' he said quickly
as she opened her mouth to deny that it was any such
thing. 'I've got to leave you now, sweetheart, but I want
you to remember—even if I don't manage to get back
down here for some time—that I don't just think you're
a great pilot...but that I also happen to love you very
much indeed,' he added softly, leaning forward to press
his warm lips to hers in a brief, gentle kiss, before rising
to his feet and quickly leaving the room.

Despite Luke's calm assurance that it was only the tail
end of the hurricane, when the storm finally struck the
island, Samantha was quite certain that it was the most

awesome and frightening spectacle that she had ever experienced. First, and almost without any warning, a violent thunderstorm filled the sky, crashing and rumbling
above their heads with such explosive noise that it was
impossible to make oneself heard. The accompanying
lightning was like nothing she had ever seen before:
rapidly flashing between the outbuildings and bounding
from tree to tree, it kept up a continuously ferocious
blaze of pyrotechnics—not unlike a firework display
which had become completely out of control.

For what seemed hours on end, the thunderous noise
assaulted their eardrums, the lightning shining almost
continuously in thick, jagged sheets of eye-scorching intensity. Both these phenomena were accompanied by a
cyclonic wind and torrents of unbelievably heavy, driving
rain that drenched everything in its path, the puddles
quickly becoming large ponds, and before long it seemed
as though the hotel was surrounded by a great lake of
water.

Huddled down in the old, stone cellars which ran beneath the hotel, the guests and servants stared at one
another in a mixture of fright and fascination over the
battle of the elements taking place outside their refuge.
Through the windows high up on the walls, it was possible to see much of what was going on, and there was a
collective groan as, despite the driving rain, the wooden
roof of the sugar mill was struck by lightning and suddenly burst into flames.

Staring at the sight, numb with shock and horror,
Samantha was almost unaware of Luke's strong arms
closing about her trembling figure, and holding her tight
as she buried her face in his shoulder, her body racked
with sobs.

That was only the precursor of what was to come, and
soon she didn't have the time to mourn the only real
home of her own that she had ever possessed. She was

far too preoccupied in trying to cope with the urgent problems arising from the loss of all light when the generator blew up, and the cellar was immediately plunged into pitch darkness. It was difficult for Luke to make himself heard, over both the screams inside the cellar and the rumbling thunder and torrential shriek of the wind, but he eventually managed to calm everyone down as she, together with Betty, Lester and Penny, quickly lit the candles which Luke had stockpiled before the hurricane struck.

As the minutes ticked by, the force of the wind seemed to redouble. The wooden shutters of the windows on the upper stories of the plantation house were ripped off the building, the shingles flying off the roof, and even from down below they could hear the boards across the windows—which had been completed only minutes before the storm arrived—crack and shatter as they were torn away. And then everything seemed to explode as the rain poured into the hotel like the sea into a sinking ship, the wind following closely to increase the mayhem and double the damage to the fabric of the building. Outside the hotel, trees were laid flat, loose branches flailing wildly about in the sky, and the guest bungalows were quickly reduced to sticks of wood and blown clean away.

Down in the cellar, many of the occupants clutched each other in terror, staring in dread and fearful fascination at the utter destruction so clearly illuminated by the continuous sheets of lightning.

If she could have made herself heard above the storm, Samantha would have been happy to publically apologise to her husband for ever having doubted his competence in an emergency. It was his planning and forethought which had provided the buckets of fresh water, enough for everyone to drink their fill as the hours ticked by; the large stack of candles—and matches—with which they kept the frightening darkness at bay; the food which he had insisted should be prepared well in advance, and the pile of newspapers which he had caused to be crumpled and placed inside the fridge and the deep-freeze cabinets, filling every inch of space before the doors and lids were shut and covered with heavy blankets, so that when the power failed—as it did—the food inside would stay cold and frozen.

Samantha was never really able to calculate the true length of the storm. Seconds, minutes and hours seemed to blend into one another as she and Betty, together with some of the other servants, made their continuous rounds of the cellar, carrying trays of sandwiches and jugs of soft drinks, and also providing something stronger for those who had clearly decided, at the onset of the storm, that they would take refuge in the anaesthetising effect of alcohol. Thanks once again to Luke's prudent foresight, there were enough mattresses and cushions to ensure that everyone was able to obtain some rest from the storm raging outside, and eventually, since there was only so much sustained fright and terror that the human brain could cope with, most of the occupants of the cellar gradually fell into a fitful, exhausted sleep.

When the dawn finally crept slowly up over the horizon, Samantha, who had fallen asleep in a chair beside the kitchen table, opened her eyes and in the dim grey light saw Luke making his way up the steps which led out of the cellar. Clutching a blanket about her shoulders, she rose and stepped carefully over the sleeping bodies on the floor as she followed him up the stairs, to enter a world that was totally unrecognisable.

'Oh—my God!' she gasped, shaking with cold as she stood in the shelter of the doorway beside Luke's tall figure, and stared about her in bewilderment. 'I—I hardly know where we are . . . I mean, of course I *know* this is the hotel, but . . .' She gestured hopelessly at the palm trees which were no longer growing upright, but lying like discarded matchsticks on the ground. And as for the lawn, it looked as if it had been ploughed up by some mechanical digger, each furrow filled with water which flowed like miniature rivers down towards the sea.

'I'm sorry about the sugar mill,' he said, putting a warm, comforting arm about her shivering figure as they gazed at the building, which had lost its roof in the fire, and which no longer seemed to possess any doors or windows.

'Yes,' she sighed, trembling with tiredness, and the chill engendered by the strong wind which was still blowing fiercely. 'It's returned to the state it was in before Aunt Emily began its restoration. Oh—goodness!' she gasped. 'I haven't had a chance to even think about her. Do you suppose they're all right on Antigua?'

He shrugged. 'I can't pretend to know the answer to that question. But I do know that, however terrible the storm last night may have been, we were incredibly lucky only to have been touched by the edge of the hurricane. If we'd been in the middle of it, I'm not sure that we would have survived at all,' he added quietly.

'But—but what's going to happen to the hotel?' she asked, looking tearfully around at the scene of total devastation.

'Well, I reckon that it's going to mean bringing in a team of bulldozers, and laying the place flat before we start trying to build it up again. There really isn't anything to save, is there?'

'Poor old Aunt Emily. I'm glad she's not here to see this.' Samantha paused for a moment. 'Barbara said... Is it really true that Aunt Em tried to stop you from seeing me?'

'She didn't just try—she succeeded,' Luke said grimly, his arm tightening about her slim figure. 'However, this isn't the time or place to discuss the machinations of your old aunt. Come on, we'd better get back. It's still not safe to stand about here,' he said, guiding her back down the steps of the cellar.

'When can we leave?' she asked, frowning through the murky grey morning light at the chaos all around her, and the fetid smell of so many bodies packed tightly together.

Luke shrugged. 'I'm not sure, but not for some hours, at least. The wind is still too strong to risk letting everyone out of the cellar just yet.'

'It doesn't look that dangerous,' she protested, hating the thought of being cooped up in the subterranean enclosure for any longer than absolutely necessary.

'Believe me, it may not look like it, but the wind is still strong enough to blow stray branches around, and there could be some nasty accidents if some of the guests are careless. My other worry is that the basic structure of many of the outbuildings has been damaged. I don't suppose you'd want to take the risk of any beams falling on . . .'

His words were interrupted by a loud shriek from Mrs Dillman. 'Where's my little darling?'

'It sounds as if Zachary Dillman has gone AWOL. That's all I need!' Samantha muttered in disgust, and then was ashamed to have been guilty of such a callous reaction as it quickly became apparent that Zachary was indeed missing.

After a concerted hunt throughout the cellars, during which no trace of the child was to be found, Mrs Dillman collapsed into a state of complete hysteria. Betty quickly took charge, slapping the poor woman's face and then, as Zachary's mother lapsed into dry sobs, she took her aside and comforted her.

'I imagine that imp of Satan had the same idea as we did, just now, and has gone outside for a breath of fresh air,' Luke quietly told Samantha. 'I'd better go and have a scout around what's left of the buildings, and see if I can find the boy.'

'For goodness' sake—be careful, Luke!' she warned him urgently, anxiously catching hold of his arm. 'Especially after what you've just said about the conditions out there.'

'Well, well...I didn't know you cared!' he grinned mockingly.

'Don't be so stupid—of course I care what happens to you,' she retorted sharply. 'In fact, I...well, I...' She hesitated for a moment.

Luke laughed. 'There's no need to worry. After surviving that flight *and* the emergency landing, I am quite convinced that you and I are totally invincible!' he drawled, lifting his hand and running a finger gently down her pale cheek. 'So, checking around the buildings for that kid has to be a piece of cake, hmm?'

With her heart in her mouth, Samantha watched Luke's crablike progress around the remains of the outbuildings. Making sure that he hugged the ground or a firm piece of masonry, he systematically searched through each nook and cranny that could conceivably shelter a small child.

'Any luck?' she called out as she caught a glimpse of him through a large crack in the wall of what had once been a garage, and was dejected when the negative shake of his head said it all. Samantha shivered as she was forced to realise that the little boy really was missing. Quite convinced that he had been either playing a game, or just sheltering within easy reach of the main house, she was now going to have to face the fact that they might not be able to locate him. She watched blindly as Luke made a final foray into the ruined remains of the sugar mill. What on earth were they going to do if Zachary couldn't be found?

Just as she was beginning to despair, and trying to brace herself for the task of relating the sad news to the Dillmans, she heard Luke give a shout. A moment later she saw Zachary crawling through the collapsed doorway of her old home. Buffeted by the wind and rain, he clung to a wooden beam, staring at her in white-faced fright.

'Lie down on the ground,' she shouted. 'Lie down and crawl around the edge of the buildings.'

For a few moments Zachary stared at her, frozen with fear, and then he slowly began to do as she said. His progress was painfully slow, but he eventually reached the entrance to the cellar, and it was a very grubby and subdued little boy who scampered down the steps, and into his mother's sobbing arms.

Following him down into the kitchen, she was pleased to see that Zachary's arrival had resulted in an immediate lifting of everyone's spirits. Penny and Betty had already got a primus stove going, and, with the prospect of some hot coffee, the occupation of the crowded cellar began to take on something of a party atmosphere. Samantha's announcement that the worst of the storm was over was received with tears and laughter, and she was relieved when everyone seemed happy to accept her report of Luke's cautionary warning about conditions outside; no one seeming anxious to leave the warmth and comfort of their temporary shelter.

'Everyone appears to be very cheerful,' she said as Betty passed a hot mug of coffee into her hands.

'Why not—since we're all going to live to see another day!' the older woman laughed happily. 'Where's that wonderful husband of yours?'

'I think he must be still outside, checking the safety of the buildings.'

'Well, I guess he's going to be cold and damp by the time he gets back, so why don't you take him up some coffee?' Betty suggested. 'And there's no need to hurry back down here. If you ask me, I reckon your Luke is a great guy, and you'd be out of your mind not to grab a permanent hold of him while the going's good!' she added with a wink, grinning at the flush spreading over the younger girl's cheeks.

Standing outside at the entrance to the cellar and waiting for Luke to reappear, it slowly began to dawn upon Samantha that something must have happened to him. Feeling sick with apprehension, she waited for a few more minutes, and then, taking a deep breath, she sank down on to her hands and knees, and began crawling slowly as she retraced the path Zachary had just taken.

No wonder the poor child had been terrified, she thought, gritting her teeth and forcing herself to ignore the frightening gusts of strong wind, and the driving rain. It seemed a lifetime before she managed to reach the shelter of the sugar mill, drenched to the skin, with her hands and knees cut by the sharp stones on the ground.

'Luke...?' she yelled, flattening herself down and wriggling in through the open doorway.

'In here,' he called out. 'I seem to have got my foot caught,' he added as she followed the sound of his voice to where he lay on the floor, with a heavy wooden beam lying across his ankle.

'Oh, lord! What happened...?'

'I guess the boy was just frightened,' he explained as she bent down to try and lift the obstruction. 'When I tried to pick him up and carry him out of here, the little monster ran away. I ran after him, but I must have dislodged that beam—and I also seem to have somehow managed to get my foot stuck in this hole.' He pointed down to where his shoe appeared to be buried in the floor.

Samantha strained, breathing heavily as she tried to lift the old oak beam. 'I don't think I'm going to be able to manage it on my own,' she panted, looking about her for something to use as a lever. 'I'd never recognise this place—not in a million years,' she muttered, staring up at the empty space where her bedroom had once been. 'Except that...heavens—how weird!' she exclaimed, staring round-eyed at the extraordinary sight of her bed, still covered with its mattress, pillows and coverlet, standing alone in the middle of the floor. 'It must have fallen down—but how come it didn't blow away with everything else?'

'It may be an interesting phenomenon,' Luke drawled. 'But if it isn't *too* much trouble, I'd like to remind you that I'm still stuck hard and fast over here.'

'Oops—sorry!' she giggled, continuing her hunt for something to act as a crow bar. A moment later she found a short length of hard wood, which she managed to lug over to where Luke was lying.

'Be careful!' he cautioned as she begin trying to jam it under the beam over his foot. 'I don't want to spend the rest of my days hobbling around with a stick.'

'Look—I'm doing the best I can, OK?' she demanded, glaring at him as she wiped the beads of sweat from her brow. 'I had to listen to you doing your "macho" impersonation all over the hotel, yesterday. So, now it's your turn to shut up, and let me try and think this through,' she added with a frown as she squatted down on her heels. 'I know that there must be a good, scientific answer to the problem—it's just a matter of working it out, that's all.'

'Oh, great! I'm going to have to lie here, drenched to the skin, while little-Miss-Fixit tries to discover the theory of relativity,' he grated. 'Let me tell you: if it's a choice between your impersonation of the Red Baron or Einstein—I'll take the Red Baron any day!'

'Too right!' she retorted grimly. 'Especially as I'm still waiting for your fulsome vote of thanks for saving your miserable life yesterday.'

He gave a harsh laugh. 'That's rich! Who shanghied me into that crazy flight in the first place? If I had any sense, I'd be happily tucked up in St Barts right now...'

'With dear Corrine, I suppose...?' she shouted angrily, furiously jamming the log she had found into the ground beside his foot.

The result of her impetuous action was spectacularly dramatic. With a loud crashing rumble of falling masonry, the floor of the sugar mill gave way, and the bed, Samantha and Luke—in that order—made a sudden and rapid descent into a deep, cavernous space below.

There was a long, shocked silence, and then Luke cleared his throat. 'OK, sweetheart. I'm willing to admit that, as far as I'm concerned, you can make the earth move more than somewhat——' He gave a husky laugh. 'But don't you think that maybe this is taking matters just a little *too* far?'

'Hmm...?' Samantha was still feeling dazed and winded, but the weight of Luke's body on hers, and the touch of his hands as they began slowly roaming over her soft curves, was having a disastrous effect on her ability to think constructively. 'What...what's happened?'

'Oh, God—who cares?' he breathed, fiercely moulding her to his strong, lean length with an urgency that made the blood race in her veins. His musky, masculine scent filled her nostrils as his lips sought and found hers, his kiss deepening with possessive force as her soft moans and the warm, yielding response of her body provoked his increasing ardour. There was a desperate hunger in his fingers as he slipped his hands beneath her T-shirt to caress and fondle her full breasts, his strong body shaking with the force of an urgent, passionate intensity barely under control.

'You belong to me!' he growled savagely as he began to strip the clothes from her body. 'You're mine—and I'm never going to let you go. *Never...ever again!*' he added fiercely, swiftly divesting himself of his own clothing.

A deep shiver of excitement rippled through her as his thick, husky voice echoed in the darkness about them. With a wordless murmur of entreaty, she wound her arms about his neck, convulsively burying her fingers in his hair as she pulled him closer to her own trembling body. Overcome by the driving force of her love and need for him, and panting for release from the tension which seemed to fill her whole existence, her body writhed and trembled beneath his strong frame, unashamedly inciting his hungry passion beyond the limits of endurance. Engrossed and absorbed by her own emotional needs, she barely heard the low, deep groans provoked from his throat by the wanton abandonment of her response. In the instant of his thrusting possession their bodies became one, igniting a mutual flame of white-hot passion which burned with scorching intensity as they instinctively acknowledged the wild, untamed hunger of their consuming need for one another.

Later, as she lay curled within the shelter of his arms, she was sleepily trying to work out exactly where they were. 'I still don't understand what happened to us,' she murmured, idly running her fingers over his long, lean legs.

'We met and fell in love again—not that I ever really stopped loving you,' he said quietly.

'No—I don't mean that...'

'Don't you love me?'

'Well, yes, as it happens, I do, but...'

'No more "buts",' he said firmly. 'I've decided that I must have been out of my mind in that aeroplane. There's no way I'm going to give you a nice, quiet divorce! You're going to stay married to me—and that's *it*!'

'Well...' Samantha grinned in the darkness as she felt him hold his breath, and the rigid tensing of his muscles as he waited for her response. 'Well...I guess I don't have much choice, do I?'

He gave a rumble of laughter. 'Oh, sure—you've got a choice. Unfortunately, it just so happens that I've *definitely* made up my mind on this matter. And you, of all people, must know just how determined and inflexible I am when I've decided I want something!'

'You're so right—I do!' she grumbled happily. 'The only thing is...' She hesitated for a moment, and then realised that nothing mattered any more, that she had no pride left as far as he was concerned. 'Yes, I do love you, Luke. I love you with all my heart, and I guess I always have. But loving is one thing, and living happily together is quite another. Do you really think we can make it work this time?'

'We'll give it a damn good try, and I promise you that it won't be my fault if it doesn't work out,' he fervently assured her, his arms tightening about her slim body. 'You were so young when we first got married, and as for me...' He sighed. 'I can now see that I was totally unreasonable in expecting you to make all the adjustments, and refusing to alter my own life in any way. When it all blew up in my face...well, I guess I was just too proud and stubborn to admit that it was mostly my fault. And I could weep for all the time we've lost— the years we've been apart. Barbara says your aunt meant well, but...'

Samantha shook her head. 'I—I still can't believe it. I mean, I really love Aunt Em, and I don't understand how she could do this to me.'

'Well, sweetheart—don't bite my head off, but I guess it's fair to say that you can be pretty convincing when you're angry. And I imagine that she must have listened to you fulminating about your rotten husband, hmm...?'

'You...you could be right,' she muttered with a shamefaced grimace.

'And I suppose that she really believed she was doing the right thing in keeping us apart. Do you know what I think?' He paused for a moment. 'I reckon that your aunt really does love and care for you—so much, in fact, that she'd have done *anything* to prevent you from getting hurt, ever again.' He sighed. 'But we can't live other people's lives for them, can we? And maybe too much love can be just as bad as too little? However, now that I've got you back again, I'm not going to hold it against the old bat,' he laughed. 'I'll either buy or build her a nice house here, on St Pauls, and we'll have her out to stay with us in the States, OK?'

'That's very kind and generous of you,' she whispered, raising her head to give him a warm kiss. 'There's only one other important thing...'

'Hmm...'

'...What about your business—and my shops?'

'As far as those shops of yours are concerned—well, it's up to you, sweetheart. I want you permanently back in the States with me, but there's nothing that says you can't come out here for flying visits, to see your aunt as well as to check on how your shops are doing. While as for my business life...' He pulled her tightly back into his arms. 'I'm not going to make any promises I can't keep,' he said slowly. 'But I am going to try and see if I can't delegate a larger part of the business to my associates, while I concentrate on my wife and—hopefully!—my children. How does that sound to you?'

Samantha sighed happily. 'That sounds just fine.'

'Mind you,' he drawled, his voice heavy with amusement, 'I can see that I'm going to be living a real dog's life with that red-haired, termagant wife of mine. It's going to be *nag-nag* and *yak-yak* all day long!'

'It's no good, Luke!' she laughed, remembering her quarrel with him back on St Barts. 'I'm feeling far too happy and contented to have any more arguments with you today.'

'Oh, dear,' he said, rolling over to trap her soft body beneath him. 'As you know, I have a low threshold of boredom, so if we aren't going to have a row, then I'll have to think of something else to do, won't I?'

'Luke!' she gasped as he began trailing his fingers over the swell of her breasts. 'We can't...! What about all those people in the cellar, for heaven's sake?'

'They're fine,' he said dismissively. 'I'm far more interested in my wife. Now I've got you to myself, I don't aim to let you go in a hurry. Unless, of course, you feel that you'd like to have an argument about whether or not I should make love to you, hmm?'

'No...' she murmured happily, as the touch of his hands became more sensual and erotic. 'No—I don't think that we're ever going to have a fight about *that* particular subject!'

This Christmas Temptation Is Irresistible

Our scintillating selection makes an ideal Christmas gift. These four new novels by popular authors are only available in this gift pack. They're tempting, sensual romances created especially to satisfy the desires of today's woman and at this fantastic price you can even treat yourself!

CARDINAL RULES – *Barbara Delinsky*
A WEDDING GIFT – *Kristin James*
SUMMER WINE – *Ethel Paquin*
HOME FIRES – *Candace Schuler*

Give in to Temptation this Christmas.
Available November 1988 Price: £5.00

Available from Boots, Martins, John Menzies, W.H. Smith, Woolworths and other paperback stockists.

THREE TOP AUTHORS.
THREE TOP STORIES.

TWILIGHT WHISPERS — *Barbara Delinsky* — £3.50
Another superb novel from Barbara Delinsky, author of 'Within
Reach' and 'Finger Prints.' This intense saga is the story of the
beautiful Katia Morell, caught up in a whirlwind of power, tragedy,
love and intrigue.

INTO THE LIGHT — *Judith Duncan* — £2.50
The seeds of passion sown long ago have borne bitter fruit for
Natalie. Can Adam forget his resentment and forgive her for leaving,
in this frank and compelling novel of emotional tension and turmoil.

AN UNEXPECTED PLEASURE — *Nancy Martin* — £2.25
A top journalist is captured by rebels in Central America and his
colleague and lover follows him into the same trap. Reality blends
with danger and romance in this dramatic new novel.

Available November 1988

◗WORLDWIDE

Available from Boots, Martins, John Menzies, W.H. Smith,
Woolworths and other paperback stockists.